HOW TO PASS

HIGHER
GEOGRAPHY

D1612820

Ian Geddes

Hodder Gibson
A MEMBER OF THE HODDER HEADLINE GROUP

Acknowledgements

The Publishers would like to thank the following for permission to reproduce copyright material:

Cartoons © Moira Munro 2005
All other artworks © Jeff Edwards 2005
All maps reproduced by permission of Ordnance Survey on behalf of The Controller of Her Majesty's
Stationery Office, © Crown Copyright 100036470

Every effort has been made to trace all copyright holders, but if any have been inadvertently overlooked the
Publishers will be pleased to make the necessary arrangements at the first opportunity.

Although every effort has been made to ensure that website addresses are correct at time of going to press,
Hodder Gibson cannot be held responsible for the content of any website mentioned in this book. It is sometimes
possible to find a relocated web page by typing in the address of the home page for a website in the URL window
of your browser.

Papers used in this book are natural, renewable and recyclable products. They are made from wood grown in
sustainable forests. The logging and manufacturing processes conform to the environmental regulations of the
country of origin.

Orders: please contact Bookpoint Ltd, 130 Milton Park, Abingdon, Oxon OX14 4SB. Telephone: (44) 01235
827720. Fax: (44) 01235 400454. Lines are open from 9.00–6.00, Monday to Saturday, with a 24-hour message
answering service. Visit our website at www.hodderheadline.co.uk. Hodder Gibson can be contacted direct on:
Tel: 0141 848 1609; Fax: 0141 889 6315; email: hoddergibson@hodder.co.uk

© Ian Geddes 2005
First published in 2005 by
Hodder Gibson, a member of the Hodder Headline Group
2a Christie Street
Paisley PA1 1NB

Impression number   10 9 8 7 6 5 4 3 2 1
Year   2010   2009   2008   2007   2006   2005

Cover photo from Science Photo Library, Image E390/323
Typeset in 10.5 on 14pt Frutiger Light by Phoenix Photosetting, Chatham, Kent
Printed and bound in Great Britain by J W Arrowsmith Ltd, Bristol.

A catalogue record for this title is available from the British Library

ISBN 10: 0 340 815817

ISBN 13: 9780 340 815816

CONTENTS

AN INTRODUCTION TO HIGHER GEOGRAPHY

Welcome To This Revision Book

So you have decided to have a go at passing Higher Geography. Good move! This already shows that you are wise, astute, discerning, intelligent, good looking …

I am biased of course, but the Higher Geography course is enjoyable, interesting and relevant to the world we live in today and will give you lots of skills that are useful for a future course or job. The examination is fair. The examining body, called the Scottish Qualification Authority (SQA), has set out in detail what you should study and know, and will then set an exam which will test you exactly on that knowledge and the skills you require. At the beginning of each section in this Book, I have printed the content of each theme. This is written mainly in the language of the SQA, although the content that follows is written for you.

How to Use this Revision Book

This is not a course book. You cannot pass the examination studying this book alone!

This book will summarise, give hints about how to study, how to pass an examination, how to revise and how to practise writing answers for the final examination. You will also find out the expected standard. It is interactive in the sense that you cannot just sit and read. You are expected to get actively involved with the book, the tasks and your other notes. If you want more information, then a few websites have been included. This book is written to help you prepare for and pass the examination. You will still need to return to your main notes and textbooks.

So what is involved in passing Higher Geography?

The boring bit! Simply put, you need to pass a number of unit assessments throughout the year, as well as the final exam in order to receive the full certificate. Higher Geography, a National Qualification Course, certificated by the Scottish Qualification Authority, consists of two 'Environment' units and one Interactions unit.

Figure 1.1

Geography: The Physical and Human Environments (Core)

There is no choice of topics in this part of the course. The word 'core' implies that the content and the skills are central to being a 'geographer'. Each topic will have been taught in short, snappy segments. Geography covers physical, human and social elements. We study our planet Earth and the people found on it. Therefore, the environment core is split into two units, Physical and Human.

Physical Environment	*Human Environment*
Atmosphere	Population
Hydrosphere	Rural
Lithosphere	Industrial
Biosphere	Urban

Geography: Environmental Interactions

Schools and colleges have a choice of the environmental interactions (applications) selected. You only need to study two interactions for the exam, but many schools/colleges will teach a third 'back-up' interaction. This Unit requires detailed knowledge, and allows you to develop the core skills in some depth and apply the ideas to a range of case study examples. There are two groups of interactions. For the Exam you should select one from each group.

Group 1	*Group 2*
Rural Land Resources	Urban Change and its Management
Rural Land Degradation*	European Regional Inequalities*
River Basin Management	Development and Health

*(Not included in this revision book)

Rural Land Degradation is not included in this revision book, but a good summary can be found in *Higher Geography Applications* by the same publishers. Alternatively, please contact Hodder Gibson for further information.

The Exam

OK, the bit that we all dread. However, the final exam in June is extremely fair. The papers are based on the syllabus, and teachers teach the syllabus. We know what is going to come up in the exam. Your job is to learn the content, think about it and then answer the questions. Simple! So what's holding you back?

There are two question papers, conveniently called Paper 1 and Paper 2 (to avoid confusion!)

Paper 1 Physical and Human Environments

Time 1 hour 30 minutes

The paper is divided into 3 sections

Section A, 4 compulsory questions

Questions 1 and 2 will be based on two of the four physical environment topics.

Questions 3 and 4 will be based on two of the four human environment topics.

Each question will be allocated 8, 9 or 10 marks. Total marks 36

Section B, 2 questions, you should select one. 7 marks

Questions 5 and 6 will be based on the two physical environment topics not assessed in Section A. You should do one.

Section C, 2 questions, you should select one. 7 marks

Questions 7 and 8 will be based on the two human environment topics not assessed in Section A. You should do one. There will be an OS map with questions covering sections, A, B or C.

Paper 2   Environmental Interactions

Time 1 hour 15 minutes

Section A, 3 optional questions, Group 1 Interactions, you should select one. 25 marks

Section B, 3 optional questions, Group 2 Interactions, you should select one. 25 marks

 So that's it! All this work for 2 hours 45 minutes of writing and 100 marks.

 ## Internal Assessment

You need to pass the Unit assessments that are slipped in throughout the teaching of the course. The questions, usually drawn from the National Assessment Bank (NAB), cover each part of the course.

SQA have also slipped in something called 'General Methods and Techniques' (GMT). In your class unit assessment you will need to show an ability to work with data presented in tables, sketches, models, flow diagrams, photographs, survey data, transects, population pyramids and graphs.

 ## The Marker

Markers will all be experienced teachers and tutors of Geography. Their work is carefully controlled and monitored by the SQA, and will be checked to ensure that similar standards are applied throughout the country. They meet to discuss answers and work from the same set of guidelines and instructions. SQA have a number of systems in place to make sure that all candidates are treated fairly. They even have an 'appeals' systems if you perform way below your best.

Believe it or not, the markers actually want you to pass. They mark what is correct and ignore what is irrelevant or wrong. The questions are never set deliberately to catch you out.

Higher Geography is marked basically in half marks. For every correct piece of information you give, you get half a mark. You do not get marks deducted for a mistake. You are expected to write in sentences, and you should avoid writing in note form, in lists or bullet points. You are positively marked if you include your own sketches, rough maps, diagrams, models or graphs. There is no need to have wonderful artistic skills; geographical information can easily be conveyed with simple visuals. However the markers can only mark what they can read. So you do need to take care with your presentation. Markers also love to see little bits of detail added and expect to see extensive reference to named case study examples. While markers do get an outline of the key points they would expect in an answer, they also have discretion to accept any appropriate correct geographical view. Part of any exam is the time limitation. You have to write under pressure. Use the full allocation of time. Do not leave early.

Key Points

An analysis of the question is important

You need to think about what you are being asked to do. I have marked too many 'perfect' answers and only awarded a low mark! The trouble is that under a little exam pressure you may not answer the question actually asked. Instead you answer something similar about what you think you were asked to do! Get a highlighter pen and clearly mark the key instructions. The active words are usually:

Account for   Explain and give reasons.

Annotate   Write notes around the diagram or photograph.

Assess   Balance and weigh up importance.

Comment on   Write an explanation and recognise the key points.

Compare   Point out similarities and differences.

Contrast   Point out the main differences.

Describe   Describe! Always state the obvious.

Discuss   Look at the evidence and comment on both sides of an issue.

Evaluate   Assess successes and failures (come to a conclusion).

Explain   Give reasons (this is not to be confused with 'describe').

Illustrate   Usually means more than draw a diagram. Can also refer to a detailed case study.

Outline   Note the main points.

Suggest   You have to give the marker your view or reason.

It is important that you know exactly what the structure of the examination is. It is generally accepted that passing an exam is more than mere knowledge. I have sat a few in my day, and fortunately have passed more than I failed! (By the way, that Physics exam I sat and failed in 1970 was an accident, a combination of bad teaching, being given the wrong notes and I genuinely thought the exam was the next week). Oh yes, blame everyone but yourself! You should find out what is involved. Get the past Papers and study the structure of the exam. But be careful. The Higher Geography examination has changed in form over the last few years, and older papers (pre-2005 will not show the current mark allocation and structure).

Questions

As a marker I have experienced a few occasions when candidates have attempted all 6 questions in the second paper. They tend not to do so well!! Nor does it please the marker, since we have to mark all the questions and give you the two highest marks. So some advice for you:

◆ Know which Interaction questions to do. I know that students sometimes have a look at some of the other Interaction questions not studied that year. Sometimes they look easier than the ones you have studied for. Can that be true? You may recognise the theme as one studied at Standard Grade, so then you think you can do it. Don't! Your answer will be pitched at too low a level. Don't take a chance.

◆ Decide which of the two Interactions you are left with, and read the whole question.

◆ Are there any easy questions? Like the *Who Wants to be a Millionaire* TV programme, they are all easy if you know the answer. I would recommend the questions with lots of diagrams, charts, tables or maps. After all, you can use the given information.

◆ Most of the Interaction questions start with an easier introductory part for 4 or 5 marks. Make sure that you read the question all the way down. The answer you give in part a may need to be expanded in parts b and c. It may well get tougher, and you will have to use in-depth case study material and detailed examples.

◆ Note the number of marks awarded.

◆ Check the 'key words' telling you what to do.

Get into the habit of analysing old questions. Think about what it is you are asked to do. I recently marked a 'prelim' paper, and noted the following ways in which normally bright pupils managed to throw away marks.

Common Mistakes

◆ A describe and explain question. They only described. Usually can only get half available marks.

◆ Using a named case study. They were vague. Usually loses 20% of available marks.

◆ With reference to a country in the 'Economically Less Developed world' (ELD world)

They referred to a country in the 'Economically More Developed World' (EMD world). Difficult to judge, but possibly no marks.

◆ Asked to draw a diagram. They didn't! Could lose half the marks

◆ Asked to be very explicit about an example given. They wrote about cholera instead of malaria

◆ There is a 10 mark question. They wrote three lines. Self-penalised, cannot get full marks.

PHYSICAL ENVIRONMENT: ATMOSPHERE CORE

(i) This is the traditional first Environment theme which appears in all the textbooks, and, indeed, I have chosen the topic for my first study. Why? Simple. It is likely to be the first question in the exam. The chances are that this was not the first Physical Environment topic you studied in class. Most schools and colleges delay teaching this theme, because it is perceived to be one of the tougher ones. That is true. However you can react in one of two ways. Some people skip so much of the atmosphere content. Not a clever move. This part requires a bit more thought. So the smart way to revise this topic is by working a little harder at it. Try to understand what is happening, rather than simply trying to memorise the content. Think about the logic. The important point to remind you of at this moment is that the questions will be taken from the key points below. I have included as SAQs all of the main questions that have come up over the years. So get out your atmosphere notes, get reading and start thinking.

What You Should Know

In the language of SQA, the characteristics of the atmosphere vary spatially and provide climate and weather conditions which interlink with other systems. In other words, what happens in the atmosphere affects climate and weather.

(i) Our planet is encased in a blanket of gases, held in place by the force of gravity. This mixture gives us our life and makes our planet unique and distinctive. There is great interest about our atmosphere in the media today. Over the course of one week, I noted the following themes in my newspaper: global warming, ozone layer depletion, hole in the ozone layer, acid rain, greenhouse effect, climatic change, CFCs, skin cancer'. So what is happening? This Physical Environment theme gives us a basic grounding in such topical environmental issues.

(!) **Check through your Atmosphere notes now.**

Questions and Answers

SAQ 1 Give a brief summary of each of the newspaper issues:

Global warming; Ozone layer depletion; Hole in the ozone layer; Acid rain; Greenhouse effect; Climatic change; CFCs; Skin cancer.

If you have Internet access, spend an hour or so "surfing".

Answer to SAQ 1

On this occasion I am not going to tell you!
We shall return to these words shortly.

SAQ 2 So what is the atmosphere? What gases make up our atmosphere?

Answer to SAQ 2

The atmosphere was formed as the Earth cooled down. Over time, the chemical composition changed and now forms a blanket around us giving us our distinctive form of life. What you need to know is that the main gases are nitrogen (78%) and oxygen (21%). The missing 1% is made up of all sorts of gases, including argon, water vapour, carbon dioxide and so on. I guess the chemists among us get excited thinking about all these gases. We'll just stick to these key ones. We'll come back later to terms such as 'greenhouse gases', but it is worth noting that the key greenhouse gases are water vapour and carbon dioxide. The atmosphere is not uniformly composed of these gases, and as we move from the surface of the Earth towards the edge of 'space' the density and amount of the air decreases, and new chemicals can be found (e.g. ozone gas); 75% of the mass of the atmosphere is within the nearest 12 kilometres of the land surface.

Solar Radiation

At 150 million kilometres away, the sun emits heat, the prime source of our energy. A tiny fraction of this reaches the Earth, giving us our energy to drive the atmospheric system, ocean currents, planetary climates and life! The diagram on the following page shows what happens to solar energy as it reaches the edge of our atmosphere. Some is reflected back into space, some is scattered and some energy is absorbed. Enough gets through to the surface to provide us with energy for life to thrive.

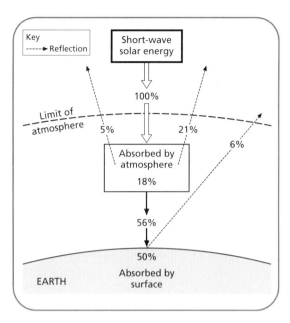

Figure 2.1 Solar radiation and energy exchange

Questions and Answers ?

SAQ 3   Study Figure 2.1, which shows Solar Energy Exchanges.

Describe and explain the energy exchanges that result in the Earth's surface absorbing only 50% of the solar energy that reaches the outer atmosphere.   *(4 marks)*

Answer to SAQ 3

Short wave solar energy called insolation is exchanged in the following manner:

Of 100% insolation energy

5% is reflected back by atmospheric gases and dust	95% left
21% is reflected back by clouds (water vapour)	74% left
6% is reflected back from the surface	68% left
18% is absorbed by the atmosphere	50% left

50% finally reaches the surface where it is absorbed

(You should note that these percentage figures tend to vary a bit from book to book, so do not be disturbed by slight variations)

However, this global heat budget balance does conceal variations on the surface. As you go from the Equator towards the Poles, there is a latitudinal variation in the heat budget.

Global Insolation

Figure 2.2 is a standard representation explaining why the tropical areas receive more solar radiation (insolation) than the polar areas. Check through your notes on all aspects of solar radiation and the surface.

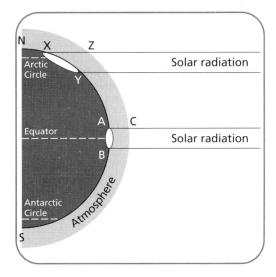

Figure 2.2 Global insolation

Questions and Answers

SAQ 4 With the aid of an annotated diagram, describe and explain why tropical areas receive more of the sun's energy than polar regions. *(4 marks)*

Answer to SAQ 4

Obviously you should draw a simple diagram similar to Figure 2.2. Your annotation should include reference to some of the points below. Remember you get half marks for each relevant point.

Imagine a 'sunbeam' arriving at the surface of the planet.

◆ In polar areas the radiation has to pass through a greater depth of atmosphere (more scope for absorption, scattering or reflecting). Compare the width of XZ and AC.

◆ Similar amounts of solar radiation cover a greater area at the Poles. Compare the areas XY with AB.

◆ You can visualise this if you switch on a torch and point it straight down at the ground. Now point the torch at a point 2 metres away. Clearly the light on the ground is less intense as the distance and angle increase.

◆ Absorption at the surface is dependent upon the 'albedo' effect (whether the surface reflects more or less radiation.). For example, a dark surface (a forest) has low reflection, and a light surface (water, sand, snow, ice) has high reflection.

◆ As you move from the Tropics to the Poles, there is variation and a decrease in the time the sun releases solar radiation over the surface.

◆ Other variables include increased sunspot activity, an increase in atmospheric dust (after a volcanic eruption), and the tilt of the Earth's axis and the varying distance of the Earth's orbit around the sun.

Questions and *Answers* continued ➤

Questions and Answers continued

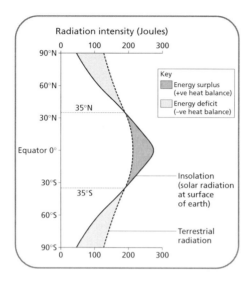

Figure 2.3 Latitude and energy balance

Answer to SAQ 4 continued

The end result is that Tropical areas have a heat surplus and there is an increasing heat deficit as you head for the Poles. This feature is often shown as a diagram.

SAQ 5   a)   Describe the latitudinal variation of the Earth's energy budget/balance shown on this diagram. *(2 marks)*

b)   Now explain this variation between the poles and the Tropics (you may draw a diagram to assist you). *(4 marks)*

Answer to SAQ 5

a)   There is a balance between incoming insolation and outgoing terrestrial radiation. Variation in terrestrial radiation from 120 joules at the Poles to 200 joules at the Equator. Low insolation total at Poles (50 joules); large energy deficit at Poles. Heat surplus and insolation high at Tropics (275 joules). Energy balanced at 35 degrees north and south.

b)   Once again the diagram would be based on Figure 2.2 on the previous page.

Tropics   High angle of sun's rays with intense heating
'Thin' layer of atmosphere for radiation to pass through
All-year incoming solar radiation
Low albedo effect (forest)

Poles   Low angle of sun's rays with low intensity heating
Thicker layer of atmosphere for radiation to pass through
Low levels of incoming radiation for much of the year
High albedo effect (ice, snow)

However this is a simple view. In reality there is movement of heat from the Tropics to the Poles. There is a transfer of heat by air and by water. Without this, the low latitudes would get even hotter and the high latitudes even colder.

Atmospheric Circulation

This looks complicated I suppose it is! However, try to search for a logical approach to this theme. The circulation of air in each hemisphere is built on the idea of three cell movements of the air.

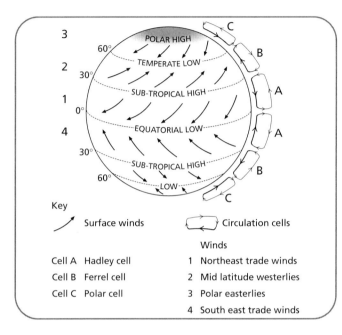

Key

↗ Surface winds   ⟲ Circulation cells

Winds

Cell A Hadley cell   1 Northeast trade winds
Cell B Ferrel cell   2 Mid latitude westerlies
Cell C Polar cell   3 Polar easterlies
                           4 South east trade winds

Figure 2.4

The key principles:

◆ Hot air rises giving low pressure.

◆ Cold air sinks giving high pressure.

◆ Air moves from high pressure to low pressure.

◆ Air is deflected by the spinning of the Earth (the Coriolis force), which means that in the northern hemisphere winds are deflected to the right, and in the southern hemisphere to the left.

Summary

 A summary of the three cell movement. Study Figure 2.4, which shows atmospheric circulation and surface winds.

Hadley Cell (Cell A)

Hot air rises (low pressure formed) and spreads north and south of the Equator. Air descends at 30 degrees north and south of the Equator, bringing cooler, high-pressure conditions. At the ground, the air either returns to the Equator or becomes part of the Ferrel Cell. Remember air moves from high-pressure areas to low-pressure areas.

Polar Cell (Cell C)

Cold dense air descends over the Poles (high pressure) and moves along the surface to lower latitudes. At around 60 degrees north and south, this air has been warmed up and rises upwards, creating a zone of low pressure. Remember the latitude numbers given are all approximate. To complete the movement we can now look at the final cell.

Summary *continued* ➢

Summary *continued*

Ferrel Cell (Cell B)

This 'middle' cell completes the circular movement. The descending air at 30 degrees north and south moves along the surface to 60 degrees north and south, bringing warmer air to those higher latitudes. This air meets the polar air and when the air masses meet, the air rises again.

The outcome of all this takes warm air to the high latitudes and feeds cold polar air back to the sub tropics for warming again.

Figure 2.4 also shows the key winds. You need to be able to recognise the trade winds, found between 30 degrees north and south (approx.). These are predictable winds affecting this large inter-tropical zone. The NE and SE trade winds converge (meet) along a line called the Inter-Tropical Convergence Zone (ITCZ). This line moves between the Tropics with the seasonal shift of the low pressure zone. It follows the line under which the sun is directly overhead. (See ITCZ notes later.)

The mid-latitude westerly winds (northern hemisphere) are essentially mild wet winds sweeping across the temperate latitudes (30 to 60 degrees north and south). The polar winds sweep from the northern areas, bringing colder unsettled conditions.

What do you need to know? Let's look at the recent questions, that have appeared in the Higher Examination.

Questions and Answers

SAQ 6   Look at the reference diagram (Figure 2.4)

Explain how the circulation cells A, B and C and the related surface winds assist in the distribution of energy over the Earth.   *(4 marks)*

Answer to SAQ 6

The core data has been summarised above.

You do need to refer to the three cells and the surface winds.

Key points

Hot air rises giving low pressure.

Cold air sinks giving high pressure.

Air moves from high pressure to low pressure.

Air is deflected by the spinning of the Earth (the Coriolis force), which means that in the northern hemisphere winds are deflected to the right.

The power behind all this is surplus heat over the Equator.

Questions and Answers continued ➤

Questions and Answers

SAQ 9 Describe the variations in global temperature over the last million years. *(6 marks)*

The key to this question is an understanding of the vertical temperature readings.

Answer to SAQ 9

Graph 1

There have been at least 15 or more noticeable cyclical changes, with warm phases followed by cold periods (Ice Ages). In context we may well still exist within an Ice Age! Stability is not a feature of this graph. The time frame within any one of these warm/cold phases could be 50,000 years or more. The striking image is that of wild fluctuations.

Graph 2

When studied over the duration of the last 20,000 years I note a 10,000-year period when the 'UK' was caught in an 'Ice Age' followed by a very rapid increase in temperature. It appears on this graph that the last 10,000 years have seen a period of stability. The striking image in this graph is the contrast between the cold phase followed by a a warm phase.

Graph 3

This graph takes us up to the last 1,000 years. Note the vertical and horizontal scales. Once again there is a variation. Following the Medieval warm period, we had a few hundred years known as the 'Little Ice Age', leading us to the last hundred or so years, when the temperatures seem to be creeping up again. This takes us to the period covered by Figure 2.6.

Conclusion

A study of the climatic data does indicate a complex pattern of variability. All the evidence does show that we now have a period of global warming. It would be logical to suggest that what is happening now is well within the 'natural' variations the planet has experienced in the past. See the physical factors above. This does not mean that we should not be concerned, because the impact and effects of global warming most certainly have far-reaching impact. However it would be foolish not to consider that 'human' activities will not have an impact upon this.

The scientists do not share one view on this. I suppose we need more information. The trouble is that we can't be sure that the information we are getting is unbiased. After all, the scientists who are researching in this area point to a problem and conclude that we need more information and more research, thereby guaranteeing them more research funding and jobs! (Or am I being too cynical?) But it seems to me that we need to do more than gather data and debate the issues. We should take action now.

What do you think?

A search through the Internet should get you into the debate.

Return to SAQ 1

★ **Global warming**   ★ **Ozone layer depletion**   ★ **Holes in the ozone layer**   ★ **Acid rain**   ★ **The Greenhouse effect**   ★ **Climatic change**   ★ **CFCs**   ★ **Skin cancer**

So what is your understanding of these terms now? This chapter has been demanding. One thing that is clear is that our atmosphere is vital to life on our planet. It does seem that with increasing technological impacts, we have the power to inflict large-scale change on this narrow band of gases and chemicals in the zone called the 'atmosphere'. It is also clear that our atmosphere has changed over the last few million years and that change must be expected in the future. However, discussion around the group of terms above does seems to indicate that we need to be aware of what we could be doing to our planet, and that we need to look to inspired leadership from our leading politicians to safeguard our future. In world terms, 2003 was the third-warmest year since records began in 1861. All 10 of the warmest years have been since 1990. Makes you think!

So what are your thoughts on the key words now? I have my own views. What is important is that you should have views yourself. Remember that the issues tend to be far more complex than the popular newspapers suggest.

The Inter Tropical Convergence Zone (ITCZ)

For some reason, this topic is the one that my students have had most concerns about. I guess that it must be my teaching! I have chosen to leave this section to the end of this chapter.

However, it is possible to take a logical approach to it. Where do we start?

What do you need to know?

◆ The role of continental tropical and maritime tropical air masses on the West African climate, particularly rainfall amounts and distribution

◆ Interpretation of climatic maps, diagrams and graphs

Let's attempt to describe the patterns using maps and graphs.

Some theory!

Check back to your notes and my summary of the Hadley and Ferrell cells. The Trade Winds converge along a line known as the Inter Tropical Convergence Zone (ITCZ) This line is not fixed and moves north and south of the Equator (known as the thermal Equator), linked to the passage of the overhead sun. When the sun is directly overhead, there is maximum heating and upward movement of the air. This results in cooling and heavy rainfall. Between March and October, the ITCZ moves from the Equator to a position 20 or so degrees north of the Equator, bringing rain to Nigeria. Between October and March, the sun is south of the Equator and the only part of Nigeria receiving rain will be in the south.

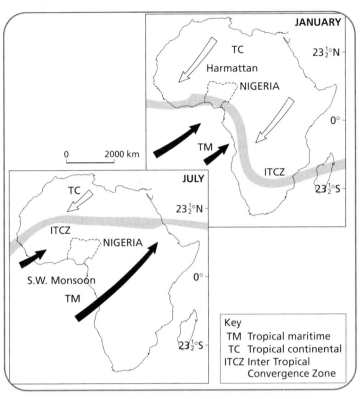

Figure 2.8 Africa: air masses and the ITCZ in January and July

As the ITCZ moves north across Nigeria, it drags behind it the Tropical Maritime air (Tm), displacing the Tropical Continental air (Tc). This means that warm, wet, southwesterly winds affect Nigeria from the south. This ITCZ line moves as far as 20 degrees north, bringing rain. The overhead sun moves south from October, pulling behind it the Tropical Continental air across the country. This means that the air is now dry, bringing drought conditions across the north of Nigeria. This dry, hot, North East Trade wind is called the 'Harmattan'.

Questions and Answers

SAQ 10 Study Figures 2.8

Describe the origin, nature and weather characteristics of the Tropical Maritime and Tropical Continental air masses. *(4 marks)*

Answer to SAQ 10

Tropical Maritime. The South Western Monsoon, originating over the Atlantic Ocean, bringing warm, moist unstable conditions. Air is humid (70 to 80%), bringing hot/very hot conditions with heavy rainfall.

Tropical Continental. The North East Trades (Harmattan) originate over the Sahara Desert, bringing warm, dry and stable air. The mass is associated with very warm/hot, dry weather with low humidity (10 to 20%).

Questions and *Answers* continued ➤

HOW TO PASS HIGHER GEOGRAPHY

Questions and Answers

SAQ 11 Study Figure 2.9

Describe and account for the variation in rainfall in the three towns across West Africa. *(7 marks)*

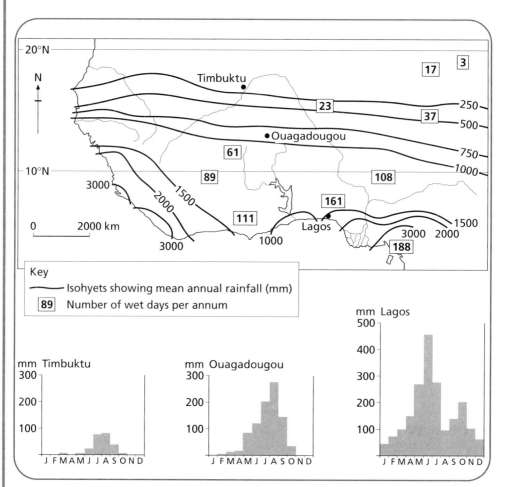

Figure 2.9 Rainfall across West Africa

Answer to SAQ 11

Some hints. You have been given a lot of information. I always advise students to look over the data and mentally go over what has been given. You have information about rainfall over a large area of West Africa. The top map shows the number of wet days per year and the isohyet lines show the mean annual rainfall in mm. The graphs show contrasting rainfall regimes for three towns. You are asked to describe the variations. The markers could award up to 4 marks for this. It is straightforward to pick up maximum marks in this task. Describe what you see.

Questions and *Answers* continued ➤

Questions *and* **Answers** *continued*

Answer to SAQ 11 continued

Timbuktu

Low total (below 250 mm) Very dry all year, slightly more rainfall July to September. Fewer than 20 days with rain per year. Long drought. Rainfall also very variable and unreliable.

Ouagadougou

(No matter what the rainfall pattern is, pause and say out loud the name of this town in Burkina Faso. What a wonderful name!) Rainfall is greater in total, (between 750 and 1,000 mm) with more wet days (around 60). Here you can see a clear dry season with a one peak maximum between May and October.

Lagos

This town has a high rainfall total (over 1,500 mm) with over 160 days with rain. The graph shows a two-peak rainfall pattern with the highest and wettest peak between March and July, with another peak in September and October. There is no dry period.

You have to explain or give an account of the reasons for the above variations.

The answer is of course linked to your understanding of the ITCZ, its passage and the influence of the Tropical Maritime and Tropical Continental air masses.

Lagos is under the influence of the warm and wet SW monsoon most of the year. The two-rainfall peak pattern is due to the ITCZ migrating northwards and then southwards again in the late summer. You need to explain the contrasting weather brought by the two air masses. Timbuktu (yes, this place does actually exist) is very close to the maximum northern limit of the ITCZ. This area is under the influence of the Tc Harmattan wind for virtually the whole year, meaning that the wet Atlantic wind seldom affects the town. Ouagadougou has its seasonal pattern due to the passage of the ITCZ. Between May and late September the ITCZ passes over this area, bringing Tm air. When the line passes south in October the hot, dry Ct air dominates.

PHYSICAL ENVIRONMENT: HYDROSPHERE CORE

 From my experience whilst marking Higher Geography papers over many years, I have noticed that this section seems to be well answered. Once again, your teacher should know exactly what is coming up in the examination. The main subject of this Core Unit concerns water, its movement and its role in the formation of landforms and landscapes.

Key Points

You should have knowledge and understanding of:

◆ The hydrological cycle:

◆ Fluvial landforms and landscapes

 That is what you have to do. I would suggest that now is a good time to find your hydrosphere notes, get them organised and read them. Hydrology is the study of water, and the hydrosphere involves studying the water element of the atmosphere and the surface of the planet.

 ## 'Water is the source of all life'

Since 1900, the population of the world has increased by 300% the demand for water has increased by 1000% and the amount of water on our planet has increased by 0%! That's the problem, and that's why knowledge and understanding of the hydrosphere is vital.

 ## Hydrological cycle

The amount of water in our planet does not alter. What does change is the property of that water, whether it be a gas, a liquid or a solid. The idea behind the cycle is that water transfers from the oceans into the atmosphere over the land, finally returning to the oceans. The processes involved are simple, including evaporation, transpiration, condensation, precipitation and run-off. While the total amount of water in the planet is fixed, nevertheless there is concern over the competing demands for its use, and its quality. Water is a sustainable resource. That means that with recycling, we can use the resource again and again. Unfortunately there seems to be human interference in the cycle that can result in environmental deterioration.

Questions and Answers

SAQ 1 Check back over key definitions and make sure you have a good grasp of:

hydrosphere, evaporation, condensation, precipitation and run-off.

SAQ 2 Put into your own words what this table shows.

Water Storage (%)

Oceans	97.5% (salt)
Other	2.5 % (fresh) of which
Ice caps	69%
Ground and soil	30.5%
Rivers/lakes	0.5%

Answer to SAQ 2

Clearly the vast amount of moisture on the planet is held within the oceans and of that only 2.5% of all water is stored as fresh water. Of that total, most of the water is locked within the Ice caps. When you consider that 30% of the fresh water is contained within the soil and the rocks beneath, then only a tiny fraction of the total water on this planet is fresh and readily available in rivers and lakes.

SAQ 3 Option A Describe with the aid of a diagram, the hydrological cycle.
(4 marks)

or

Option B Study Figure 3.1.

Explain how a balance is maintained within the hydrological cycle.   *(4 marks)*

Answer to SAQ 3 Option A

The diagram should be the width of the page and ideally no smaller than a third of the page. I prefer drawings in pencil, with some colour. However you need to work quickly and you should remember that this is not an art exam, and roughness is a likely outcome. The diagram (according to the guidance markers have been given over the years) should include reference to:

◆ Evaporation/transpiration

◆ Condensation

◆ Infiltration/run-off/melting

◆ Storage i.e. ice, ground water, oceans, rivers/lakes

◆ Precipitation, plus mention of the movement around the hydrological cycle

Questions and *Answers* continued ➢

Questions and Answers continued

Answer to SAQ 3 Option B

Obviously this diagram has far too much information within it. The balance is maintained by the cycle contained within the diagram, and you can mention the key processes, (precipitation evaporation/ transpiration, condensation, infiltration/run-off/melting, storage: i.e. ice, ground water, oceans, rivers/lakes)

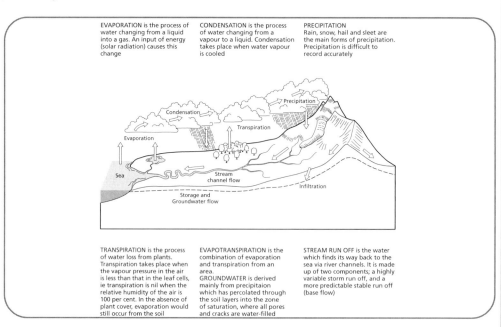

Figure 3.1 Hydrological cycle

Drainage Basin

A drainage basin is the 'catchment area' of a stream and its tributaries. The boundary is called the 'watershed'. The drainage basin is best viewed as a system with

- **Inputs**   Moisture entering the system, i.e. precipitation

- **Storage**   Moisture contained within the system in the soil, vegetation, lakes, ice, rivers and ground

- **Output**   All moisture which leaves the system: e.g. by evaporation, or entering the sea

- **Transfers** This is the movement through the system, for example within the air, by precipitation, ground seepage and infiltration.

Within the river basin, water erosion, transportation and deposition create the distinctive valley and channel characteristics. While all rivers and their basins are different, it is possible to identify a model of a typical river divided into three stages: the upper course, the middle course and the lower course.

Erosion	Main erosion processes: – lots of energy required to keep the process active 1. Hydraulic. The sheer force of water causes an increase in pressure, resulting in material being dragged from the bed and banks of the river. 2. Corrasion. The 'sandpaper' effect where sediment scours and wears away the river bed and river banks causing a collapse. 3. Corrosion/solution. Where rocks (such as limestone) lining the river bed and banks slowly get dissolved in the weak acidic waters. 4. Attrition. The wearing away of rock/ fragments already in the river as they collide with each other, breaking into smaller pieces.
Transportation	Main processes: – transportation requires high energy levels to sustain the movement 1. The dissolved load of the river can be carried in solution. 2. Fine-grained, light-weight material can be carried in suspension. 3. Debris can be bounced (saltation) along the river bed, pushed, or rolled (traction).
Deposition	When energy levels drop, the transported load is deposited or dumped. This happens when: 1. Rivers reach their base level, the sea/a loch. 2. The river overflows onto a flood plain. 3. At low energy points such as the inside of meander. 4. A general drop in the level of a river, e.g. during a drought. 5. Where there is decrease in gradient, e.g. below a waterfall.

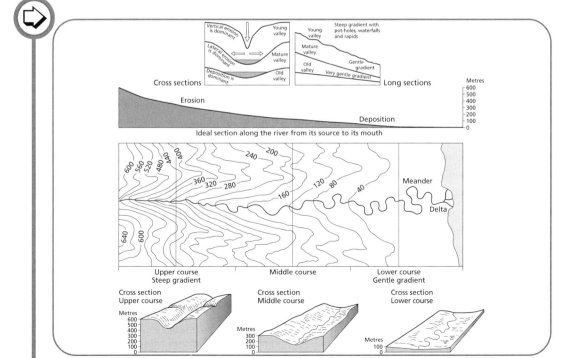

Figure 3.2 Features of a model river basin

HOW TO PASS HIGHER GEOGRAPHY

Key words of a model river basin:

Upper course	Middle course	Lower course
Rocky, uneven river bed with numerous boulders. River gradient usually steep but varies with rock type. River flow and speed can be low or high depending on precipitation. Mainly vertical erosion with hydraulic and corrosion action. Very little deposition. Valley has steep sides, 'V' shape, narrow bottom, interlocking spurs, and channel filling most of valley floor. Features include potholes, waterfalls, rapids, plunge pools	Smoother river banks and bed. River is wider and deeper. River gradient is more gentle. River flow has more water in it. Little vertical erosion but some lateral erosion on banks. Narrow flood plain. Blunt valley spurs with some meanders. Features include meanders, occasional (less spectacular) waterfall. River has certainly lost its 'wild phase'.	The river in this stage is at its broadest and deepest, gradient gentle. Erosion on the outer bends of river meanders and on the flood plain. Deposition however is the dominating action. Valleys can be many kilometres wide with well eroded bluffs and valley bottom flat. River channel can be choked by deposition. Features include floodplains, natural levees, braided channels, eyots, many and wider meanders, ox bow lakes, pools and riffles, estuaries, deltas.

Of course this is not new. Hard-working geography students such as yourself, (!) first probably covered some of this in second year, repeated it in more detail at Standard Grade, and here we are looking at it again. So what are we asking now?

Questions and Answers

SAQ 4   Choose **one** part of the river's course, (upper or middle or lower) and explain the effects of flowing water in terms of erosion, transportation and deposition.   *(4 marks)*

Answer to SAQ 4

The answer is taken from the two tables on page 28 and 29. However you can probably realise that there is far more to say about the lower stage. That is true when you also consider some other questions. The most frequently asked question requires you to recognise these features on an OS map. You need to be able to apply the knowledge contained above. You should check through your notes and have a look at examples already studied.

Questions and *Answers* continued ➤

Chapter 3

Questions *and* Answers *continued*

SAQ 5   Study Figure 3.3, Map Extract: Ellesmere Port

Examine the course of the River Gowy between 467670 and its mouth at 431775. Describe the evidence that would suggest that the river in this section is in its lower course.   *(4 marks)*

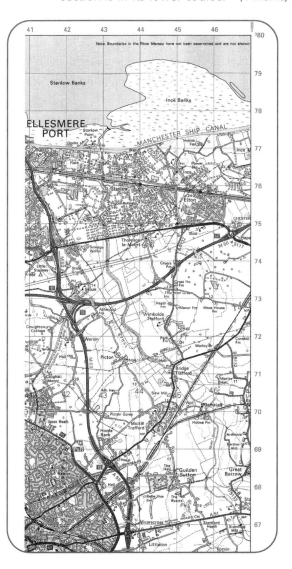

Figure 3.3   Map extract: Ellesmere Port

Answer to SAQ 5

The question could also have asked you to describe the features you can see. So what should you do? Believe it or not, you can get up to 1 mark for giving (2) correct and appropriate grid references.

Questions and *Answers* continued ➤

PHYSICAL ENVIRONMENT: HYDROSPHERE CORE

Questions and Answers continued

Answer to SAQ 5 continued

So, what is the evidence?

◆ A gentle gradient. Note 12 metres spot height (465672) to 0 metres.

◆ River joins the sea at 431775.

◆ Several meanders, e.g. in 4275.

◆ A broad, flat flood plain, e.g. 4372 with surrounding low lying land.

◆ Tidal with extensive mudflats, e.g. 4377.

◆ Drainage ditches, levees and embankments e.g. 4374.

You also need to tie up what you see on the map as features that you would expect to see of a typical river in its lower stage.

SAQ 6   Study Figure 3.4, Map extract: Afron Dysynni

Using appropriate grid references, describe the physical characteristics of the Afon (River) Dysynni and its valley from 710094 to 608050 (at the point it leaves the map).   *(4 marks)*

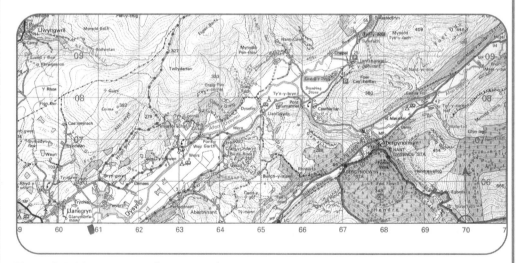

Figure 3.4 Map extract: Afon Dysynni

Answer to SAQ 6

This is a mountainous area, and it is easy to see plenty of examples of mountain streams in the upper stage of a river's development. However the question relates to a river in a glaciated, mountainous area. In fact the bulk of the features visible are those to be expected in the lower stages of a river.

Questions and *Answers continued* ➤

Questions and Answers *continued*

Answer to SAQ 6 continued

◆ The river is contained within a steep-sided, flat-floored U-shaped river valley, e.g. 300 metres wide in 6908, and 1 kilometre in 6205.

◆ Several meanders are found, e.g. at 708089 and 612052.

◆ Flows in a general SW direction and river joined by several tributaries, e.g. 675072.

◆ Differential erosion likely to have caused the narrowing of the valley between 675072 and 662078 (band of hard rock?).

◆ Misfit stream.

◆ Evidence of artificial drainage channels and ditches in 6305.

SAQ 7 Select a feature traditionally found in the upper stages of a river and its valley (or from the map extract) and, with the aid of an annotated diagram, explain its formation. *(4 marks)*

or

SAQ 8 Select a feature that you have identified from the OS map, or associated with the lower stage of a river, and with the aid of an annotated diagram, explain its formation. *(4 marks)*

Answer to SAQ 7

If you check through the list of features found in the upper stages of a river, I think that the best feature to describe is a waterfall. Copy my sketch and add the words in the appropriate places

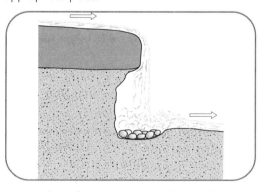

Figure 3.5 Waterfall

◆ Hard overlying resistant rocks (e.g. limestone).

◆ Softer more easily eroded rock (e.g. mudstone).

◆ River dropping into (plunge) pool, hydraulic action and abrasion.

◆ Erosion which over time results in undercutting.

◆ Harder overlying rocks collapse.

◆ Process repeated and the waterfall 'moves' upstream.

Questions and **Answers** *continued* ➤

Questions and Answers continued

Answer to SAQ 8

If you have a fairly open choice, then make sure you select a relevant feature about which there is lots to write. If you check through the characteristic features (floodplains, natural levees, braided channels, eyots, meanders, ox bow lakes, pools and riffles, estuaries, deltas), I would suggest that you perfect your drawings and notes for meanders and ox bow lakes.

Hydrographs

You need to be able to construct and analyse hydrographs and present and interpret river flow data.

There is a direct relationship between precipitation and river runoff. You do not need to have studied Geography for 5 or 6 years to work out that rivers tend to run higher after heavy rain. It's obvious! Geographers however need to go beyond the obvious. The table below shows the variables that influence the infiltration of water into river systems. Geography is a social science, and that means we go beyond simple descriptions. We like to apply a scientific approach, and to assist us in an analysis of precipitation and river flow/runoff we can construct tables and graphs to illustrate the relationship, which is usually shown on a diagram called a 'hydrograph'.

Surface Run-Off Variables

Rapid run-off or discharge	Variables	Slow run-off or discharge
Little or none	Vegetation	Dense cropland/Forest
Impermeable rock e.g. granite	Rock type	Permeable rock, e.g. chalk
Steep	Slope	Gentle or flat
Urban/built-up environment	Ground cover	Farmland
Very close to the surface	Depth of water table	Deeper down into the ground
Heavy and intensive	Precipitation	Low or gentle
Low temperatures	Evaporation	High temperatures

Figure 3.6 shows a model hydrograph. Take note of the information shown. It matches time with precipitation and river run off/discharge levels. (Note that the unit of measurement of discharge is 'cubic metres of water per second, cumecs.)

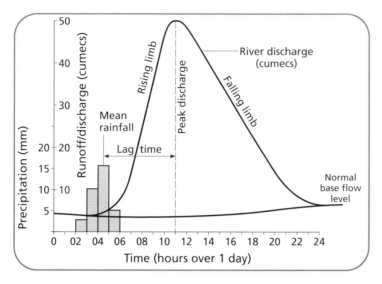

Figure 3.6 Hydrograph showing main features of precipitation and river discharge

Questions and Answers

SAQ 9   Describe the relationship between rainfall and discharge.   *(4 marks)*

Answer to SAQ 9

Between 0200 and 0600 hours there was precipitation reaching a maximum of 15 millimetres falling in the hour between 0400 and 0500 hours. The river has a seasonal base flow of 5 cumecs. Within an hour of the rain starting to fall, the level of the river started to rise quickly (rising limb), reaching a peak discharge of 50 cumecs after 5 to 6 hours. It took another 12 hours (falling limb) before the river returned to its normal base-flow level.

Over the last decade or so, we seem to be increasingly prone to flooding. Why should this be so? Flooding tends to occur when the surface run off is high and fast, and the sudden surge in the level of the river cannot be contained. As a society we increasingly speed up that rate by, for example, building roads and by cutting down trees. However we also allow houses, factories and development to take place within the area of a river's flood plain. So when a river is high, where will it flood? Can we really be surprised when flooding takes place in a new housing estate (usually called 'The Meadows' or 'River View'!) built alongside and within the old flood plain of the river?

To reduce the rush of flooding, we need to look at ways in which we increase the 'time lag' and to make the 'rising limb' less steep. We can do this by continuing to 'control' the river. I have to say however that although we may think we are smart enough to do this, the reality is that ultimately the raw and unpredictable power of nature will always create havoc.

Questions and Answers

SAQ 10 Study Figure 3.7. Describe and account for the changes in the discharge levels of the River Irvine between 21 and 22 October 2003.

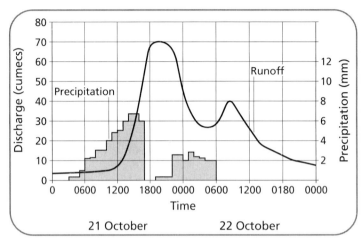

Figure 3.7 Discharge of River Irvine between 21 and 22 October 2003

Answer to SAQ 10

- Essentially you have to show that you can describe the data showing change in precipitation over the 2 days.
- Similarly, you need to be able to describe the changes in discharge levels over the same time.
- You need to be able to link up the two sets of data and offer some reasons.
- Recognise the existence of a base flow/run-off of around 5 cumecs.
- Note the increase in flow following precipitation from 5 cumecs to a peak of 70 cumecs.
- The river starts to rise around 6 hours after the start of the rain.
- You can calculate the 'lag time' (from maximum precipitation to peak discharge) as around 3 hours.
- Mention the 'rising limb', peaking at around 70 cumecs on the 21st shortly after 1800 hours.
- Note the high levels being maintained for 3 or 4 hours before the 'falling limb' is seen.
- Note that the second peak mirrors the same pattern and relationship, but peaks at a lower level (40 cumecs).
- A period without rain allows the river to return to the base flow level.
- Speed of run-off is linked to the factors summarised in the 'surface run off variables' table above.

Another way of checking your understanding of hydrographs could involve giving you two graphs of contrasting rivers and asking you to describe and account for the differences.

PHYSICAL ENVIRONMENT: LITHOSPHERE

Geography studies the physical landscape. It may seem that our coast, mountains, slopes and rivers do not change, but over millions of years this country has seen amazing transformations. Scotland has the remains of volcanoes and violent crustal action, sandy beaches and coastal cliffs, glaciated mountains and lowlands, evidence of old desert dunes, remnants of tropical forests, and the fossil remains of creatures that once swam in tropical seas.

What You Should Know

The main idea is that the lithosphere displays a range of landforms and patterns, which can be explained by reference to a variety of processes on different scales. You should have a knowledge and understanding of:

◆ Glaciated upland, coasts and upland limestone, and should include:

◆ The formation of the characteristics of these landscapes.

◆ The identification of landscape features from OS maps.

Revision of some key ideas

To assist you in this Core, you need to check your notes on a number of important ideas. While you will not get specific questions on the following topics, you do need an understanding of the 'cycle of erosion'.

Mountains are formed and then subjected to the forces of erosion and weathering. The land is eroded by the action of water and ice, by wind, by the sea and from human action. The eroded material is transported and then deposited in valleys, lakes and the sea.

Weathering is usually defined when physical, chemical and biological processes cause rocks to become loose and break down into the regolith. Check back on the action of frost shattering, freeze-thaw and onion weathering (exfoliation).

Rocks can be categorised as:

igneous (fire formed and generally hard and resistant) such as basalt or granite,

sedimentary (formed from the sediments of water deposits) such as limestone, sandstone or coal, and thirdly

metamorphic (rocks changed by extreme heat or pressure) such as gneiss, marble or schist.

You should note that there is overlap between the contents of this Physical Environment Unit and the Lithosphere and the Environmental Interaction Unit, Rural Land Resources. You should check through your coastal notes now.

HOW TO PASS HIGHER GEOGRAPHY

Coastal Scenery

Most of us live within an hour of the coast, so knowledge and understanding of the main features is relevant. In Scotland, we have a rich variety of coastal landscapes – long sandy beaches in Fife, high cliffs in Caithness and drowned glaciated valleys in Argyll. For Higher Geography you have to have a good knowledge and understanding of the processes leading to coastal erosion and deposition.

Questions and Answers

SAQ 1   Match the 4 coastal erosion processes (Column A) with the description (Column B)

Column A

A Hydraulic pressure

B Corrasion

C Attrition

D Corrosion/solution

Column B

1. The chemical weathering of the cliff when salts and weak acids dissolve the rock minerals.

2. The sheer force of the waves as they crash into a cliff, explode, compress the air and cause the face to break up.

3. The 'sandpaper' effect when waves, armed with rocks and pebbles rub away the base of the cliff.

4. Rocks and pebbles rub against each other on the beaches forming smaller and smaller particles.

Answer to SAQ 1

A=2, B=3, C=4, D=1

Landform 1 Cliffs and Wave-Cut Platforms

When high land juts into the sea, a cliff is formed. At the base of the cliff, between the low and high tide marks, erosion is at its maximum under the impact of corrasive, corrosive and hydraulic action.

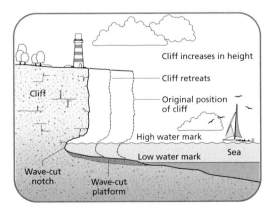

Figure 4.1 Wave-cut platform, wave-cut notch

Questions and Answers

SAQ 2 Describe what is happening in Figure 4.1. *(4 marks)*

Answer to SAQ 2

A notch is cut into the base of the cliff and, over time, this notch gets larger and deeper, mainly by hydraulic action. Eventually the unsupported rock above will collapse into the sea. The sea will remove this debris, and the process repeats itself. Eventually a wave-cut platform will be left in front of the cliff, which is now retreating.

Landform 2 Headlands and Bays

Rock type can influence the rate of erosion. Headlands and bays occur where you get alternative bands of hard (resistant) and soft (less resistant) rocks. The basic rule is that softer rocks (such as glacial clays) are associated with bays and beaches, while harder rocks (such as granite, chalk or shale) form headlands, cliffs and stacks. In time, the headlands receive the highest energy waves and become more vulnerable to erosion than the sheltered bays, where low energy waves lead to the build up of a sandy beach.

Landform 3 Caves, arches and stacks

Questions and Answers

SAQ 3 Study Figure 4.2, and describe the processes and stages involved in the creation of a stack and a stump. *(5 marks)*

An alternative to this question would ask you to draw such a diagram to show the processes involved.

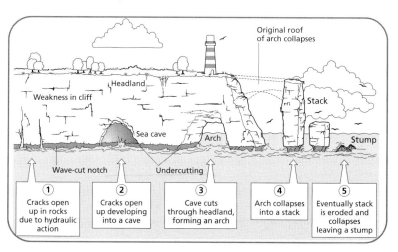

Figure 4.2 Caves, arches and stacks

Questions and *Answers* continued ➤

Questions and Answers continued

Answer to SAQ 3

There are five stages in the creation of a stack and stump.

Stage 1	The sea opens up a crack in the rock (point of weakness) by hydraulic action.
Stage 2	The cracks get larger, deeper and wider, developing into a cave. Note the creation of a notch, with the undercutting of the cliff.
Stage 3	The sea now attacks the cave and the raw power can cause the cave to open up right across the headland, forming an arch.
Stage 4	Continuing erosion will eventually cause the arch to collapse into the sea, leaving behind a self-standing stack. As this stack is now exposed to the sea, undercutting continues to erode the stack, which becomes smaller (called a 'needle').
Stage 5	And then finally the stump is left and the needle collapses into the sea.

Coastal Deposition

The main features formed by deposition are beaches, sand spits, sand bars and tombolos. Briefly we need to consider the process of transportation. The materials to be deposited are carried by the waves. The origin of such deposits will be the rock fragments from the eroded cliffs and the subsequent attrition of those fragments into smaller deposits.

Questions and Answers

SAQ 4   Study Figure 4.3, which shows the processes involved in transporting materials along a beach. Describe and explain what is happening.   *(4 marks)*

Alternatively, you could be asked to draw a diagram showing the process. Practise drawing this diagram.

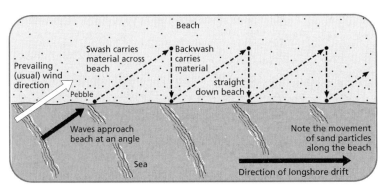

Figure 4.3
Transportation of materials along a beach

Questions and Answers continued ➤

Questions and Answers continued

Answer to SAQ 4

The diagram is almost self-evident. However one of my students answered it like this.

'If you imagine a grain of sand being swept along in a wave being driven by the prevailing wind, then that grain is carried up the beach at an angle by the swash. Then when the swash runs out of energy, the backwash returns straight down the beach, back to the sea. The outcome of this is that in time that grain of sand and thousands of other grains get swept along the beach. The movement of the waves is called longshore drift'.

Landform Beaches, sand spit, sand bar and tombolo

Beaches form where wave energy is low and deposition of mud, silt, sand, shingle and boulders take place. We tend to think of a beach as being sandy, but really a beach is defined as an area where the sea deposits material. The size can vary from the smoothest mud, through 'gritty' sand to boulders the size of your head! The order of deposit upon a beach is all down to energy levels. The swash carries all materials up the beach. The backwash tends to have less energy and can usually only pick up the small light deposits (mud, silt or sand). The heavier shingle and boulders are deposited by storm waves and tend to remain stranded furthest from the sea.

Questions and Answers

SAQ 5 Describe and explain the processes involved in creating a sand spit, sand bar and tombolo. *(3 marks)*

Answer to SAQ 5

A spit is a deposition feature (mud/sand/shingle) built out from the land from a headland or river estuary. The conditions required will include.

◆ Active longshore drift with a source of sand/shingle.

◆ A coastline with a change of direction allowing a sheltered area for deposition.

◆ Shallow water across a bay or estuary.

Over time the sand/shingle builds up in the sheltered water. It is as if the beach has been extended out into the bay. The fast waters from the river ensure that the sand spit does not extend across the bay. However when the river is sluggish, it may be that the sand can deposit faster than any erosion and a sand bar is formed. Between the land and the bar a pool of stagnant seawater will form (called a lagoon). The final feature is a tombolo. This happens when a sand spit extends from the main land across to an island. Usually this feature is covered by the water at high tide, but is exposed at low tide, and you could walk to the little island. (mind you, this is not recommended due to the changing nature of the tides and the properties of the deposits).

HOW TO PASS HIGHER GEOGRAPHY

OS maps and coastal processes and landforms

It is possible that you could be given a map with coastal features. You could be asked to recognise the key features described above as well as being asked to explain the processes involved.

Mountain or Carboniferous Limestone

Introduction

Check out a map showing the main mountain limestone areas in the UK (Yorkshire Dales, Peak District). Limestone is a hard, grey, permeable, sedimentary rock formed under the sub-tropical seas 340 million years ago.

Although a resistant rock, the calcium carbonate reacts with rainwater resulting in a distinctive landscape. As the limestone dries, horizontal layers take shape (bedding planes) and vertical cracks (called 'joints') form. The rain seeps into the joints and runs along the bedding planes, dissolving the limestone. The limestone was squeezed into rugged mountains (over 500 metres high), and over the last 2 million years subsequently affected by glacial erosion.

You should check through your mountain or carboniferous limestone notes now.

Questions and Answers

SAQ 6   Jot down meanings for the following limestone words:

Limestone pavement, clints, grykes, swallow hole, spring line, scar, stalactites, stalagmites, caves, gorge, dry valley

Answer to SAQ 6

Summary of key carboniferous mountain features

Limestone pavement	The flat surface (scraped bare by glaciers and dissolved by rainwater) of flat-topped blocks or *clints* and cracks called *grykes*.
Drainage patterns	Generally, rivers flowing onto limestone, sink into the rock, leaving a *swallow, pot or sink hole*. The surface is free from drainage, with the rivers emerging at a *spring line* at the base of the limestone (*resurgence*).
Scar	Thick slabs of limestone (up to 200 metres thick) often form a sheer cliff face.

Questions and *Answers* continued ➤

Questions *and* Answers

Answer to SAQ 6 continued

Cavern or cave	Underground passages open up by the action of the water. Within the cavern/cave, dripstone deposits result in *stalactites* (from the ceiling), *stalagmites* (from the ground) and *rock pillars*. Sometimes a cave system collapses forming a *gorge*.
Dry gorges and dry valleys	During the Ice Age, huge amounts of water passed over the frozen ground cutting out deep valleys and *gorges*. Once the glaciers melted and the ground thawed, the 'dry' features remain visible today.

SAQ 7 Study the sketch diagram (Figure 4.4) of a carboniferous limestone landscape.

Select two features from the following list and explain the processes involved in their formation:

- ◆ Limestone pavement
- ◆ Stalactites and stalagmites
- ◆ Gorge   *(8 marks)*

Alternatively you might be asked to draw one or more of these limestone features. So make sure you practise your sketching.

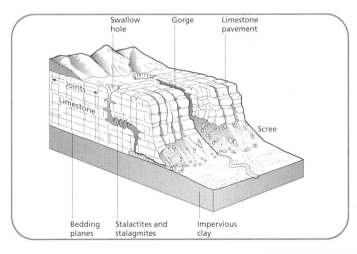

Figure 4.4 Carboniferous limestone landscape

Questions *and* Answers continued ➢

Questions and Answers continued

Answer to SAQ 7

Limestone pavement

◆ Carboniferous limestone scraped clear of soil and glacial drift by glacial erosion (abrasion).

◆ Limestone, over time, dries out, contracts and forms joints and lines of weakness.

◆ Along and down such weakness joints, chemical weathering (weak carbonic acid from rainwater) selectively works by widening these joints into clints (the raised blocks) and grykes (the deep cracks).

Stalactites and stalagmites

◆ Stalactites grow from the ceiling and stalagmites from the ground.

◆ The features are linked to the movement of water underground and the system of joints.

◆ Found in caves and caverns where the underground water is rich in lime.

◆ Water percolates and drips through the rocks. As the lime-rich water drips down some evaporation takes place, leaving behind redeposited lime hanging as little 'icicles' (stalactites) and as little stumps (stalagmites) at the point the drip strikes the ground.

◆ Rock pillars form when the stalactites and stalagmites meet.

Gorge

◆ Opinions vary, but probably caused by a roof collapse in areas where there has been active underground erosion of the caverns. This may have followed glacial meltwater surges when massive amounts of water flooded limestone areas. The joints were enlarged and passages, shafts and caves formed, then collapsed.

◆ Gorges also tend to follow the line of a weak joint.

◆ From the collapsed cavern, a dry valley is left. But once again rapid downward erosion continues when rivers flow across the area.

◆ An alternative explanation is that gorges can also be the outcome of a retreating waterfall.

This is a common question. You could also have a few simple little diagrams ready to show the markers that you know what is happening.

The two main agents of erosion in a mountain or carboniferous limestone area are ice and water.

Questions and Answers continued ➤

OS Maps and Limestone

It is possible that you could get a carboniferous limestone OS map question. What could you be asked to do? Essentially you will be asked to look at the map and recognise the evidence and provide a broad description of the key limestone features. Use grid references and only refer to features that are named or obvious on the map. Usually you can see swallow holes, potholes, shake holes, scars, springs, disappearing streams, gorges, caverns and limestone pavement.

Glaciated Upland Landscapes

Over the last 3 million years our country has been repeatedly covered and cleared of ice sheets and glaciers. This period (the Pleistocene) also includes what we call 'the Ice Age'. It is difficult to imagine that a mere 15000 years ago, where you are seated now was under some thousand or so metres of ice. The main upland areas include the Highlands of Scotland (including the Grampians and Cairngorms), the Lake District and Snowdonia.

Check through your Higher glaciated mountain notes now.

You should also note that much of Europe was also affected by ice, and you can still see 'live' glaciated scenery in countries such as Switzerland, Iceland and Norway.

Glaciers erode, transport and deposit

Once glaciers have passed over an area it is changed forever.

The main glacial erosion processes include

◆ **Frost shattering** – the action of ice (freeze thaw process) causes rocks to be loosened and can result in rocks shattering and forming a scree slope, or be further eroded by abrasion and plucking.

◆ **Abrasion** – when rocks under a glacier are worn away by the grinding action of the rock fragments being carried and embedded in the glacier.

◆ **Plucking** – ice freezes and sticks to rocks and when the ice moves, large pieces of rock are pulled away with the ice.

Questions and Answers

SAQ 8   Make a list of the main erosion features you can remember. Aim for 8.

Make a list of the main deposition features you can remember. Aim for 5.

Answer to SAQ 8

Check your list against mine. (No cheating!) Those features marked* are the ones that have featured in the exam (so far), and you certainly do need to know the processes involved in the formation of these features.

Questions and **Answers** continued ➤

PHYSICAL ENVIRONMENT: LITHOSPHERE

Chapter 4

41

Questions *and* Answers *continued*

Answer to SAQ 8 continued

Erosion		Deposition (by ice and meltwater)	
Corrie (Cwm/cirque)	*	Moraine (terminal *, medial and lateral)	
Hanging valley	*	Erratics	
Arête	*	Outwash (plain)	
Roche moutonnée	*	Alluvial fan	*
Glacial trough		Esker	*
Ribbon lake		Drumlin	*
Truncated spur		Scree	*
Pyramidal Peak		Kettles	
Corrie lochan	*	Kame	
Striations		Boulder clay (till)	
(Misfit stream)			

SAQ 9 Now write a description and a brief explanation of the processes for each of the following features:

Erosion Corrie (Cwm/cirque), Hanging valley, Arête, Roche Moutonnée, Glacial trough, Ribbon lake, Truncated spur, Pyramidal peak, Corrie lochan, Striations

Deposition Moraine (terminal), Erratic, Outwash (plain), Alluvial fan, Esker, Drumlin, Scree, Kettles, Kame, Boulder clay (till)

Answer to SAQ 9

Feature of Erosion	Description	Process
Corrie (Cwm/cirque)	'Armchair' hollow in mountainside with steep back wall and a 'rock lip'.	Frost shattering, abrasion, plucking and rotational ice movement.
Hanging valley	Tributary glacier left high above the main valley.	Ice in main valley far more active than ice in tributary glacier which lacks same erosion power (often leaving a waterfall)
Arête	Narrow, knife-edged ridge	Two corries cut back towards each other.
Roche moutonnee	Ice-smoothened rocks with a rougher steeped side facing down-valley.	Abrasion on the side facing direction of the glacier and plucking on down-valley side.

Questions *and* Answers *continued* ➤

Questions and Answers continued

Answer to SAQ 9 continued

Feature of Erosion	Description	Process
Glacial trough	Steep-sided U-shaped valley.	Widened and deepened by valley glaciers.
Ribbon Lake	Long narrow lake in glacial trough.	Over-deepening, then flooding of glacial trough.
Truncated spur	High, steep cliff valley side.	Valley glacier erodes the ends of interlocking spurs.
Pyramidal peak	Pointed peak with arêtes radiating outwards.	Three or more corries cut back towards each other.
Corrie lochan	Small, deep, circular loch within a corrie.	Downward rotational erosion, leaving hollow trapped behind rock lip.
Striations	Rocks scarred with thin scratches.	Hard rocks dragged over exposed rocks.
Misfit stream	Small post-glacial river in the large glacial trough.	
Moraine	Moraine is the general name for the material carried and dumped down by the glacier.	Lateral when dropped at the side of the glacier, terminal at the end.
Erratics	A large boulder left in an unnatural situation.	Picked up by the glacier, moved to a new location and subsequently deposited.
Outwash (plain)	Gravel, sand and clays found downstream from a glacier.	Sorted, carried and subsequently deposited by the meltwater rivers emerging from a glacier.
Alluvial fan	A fan-shaped pile of debris at mouth of river.	When a river leaves mountain stage, the gradient drops, and the river is unable to carry the same load. Deposition of materials occurs.
Esker	Long, narrow, sinuous ridges of coarse sands and gravels.	Probably old sub-glacial melt water channel, formed when glacier retreating.
Drumlin	Smooth, elongated mounds of boulder clay (till).	Debateable. Overloaded glacier drops material which is then smoothed and rounded by ice passing over the low hill.

Questions and *Answers* continued ➤

Questions and *Answers* continued

Answer to SAQ 9 continued

Feature of Deposition	Description	Process
Scree	Unsorted pile of rocks usually at the base of steep slope.	Frost shattering and rocks falling through gravity to form a slope.
Kettle (hole)	Depressions, often filled with water.	Blocks of ice left by retreating glacier and partially buried. When the ice melts a hollow is left.
Kame	Undulating mounds of sand and gravel.	Deposited unevenly, but sorted, by the meltwater along the front/side of a glacier.
Boulder clay (till)	Unsorted mixture of rocks, clays and sands.	Largely transported as ground moraine and deposited by the glacier as it retreated.

Of course this is only a summary of those key erosion and deposition features. As I have indicated above, you can be selective. Let's have a look at a typical question.

SAQ 10 Study reference Figure 4.5, which shows a landscape with both glacial erosion and glacial deposition features.

Select one feature of erosion and one feature of deposition and explain the processes involved in the formation of each feature. *(6 marks)*

Erosion features

Arête

Corrie

Hanging valley

Roche moutonnée

Deposition features

Drumlins

Terminal moraine

Esker

Alluvial fan

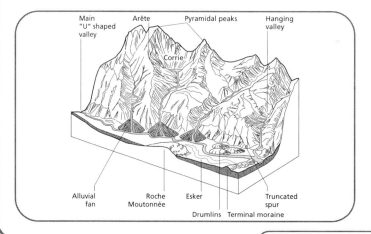

Figure 4.5 A glaciated landscape

Questions and *Answers* continued ➤

Questions and Answers continued

Variation of SAQ 10   Select any feature of erosion (or deposition) and, with the aid of annotated diagrams, explain how it was formed.   *(4 marks)*

Answer to *SAQ 10*

Although a sketch diagram was not asked for in the basic SAQ, you should always consider drawing something simple.

You can of course select which features to explain. However it is clear that you could write lots for a corrie and for terminal moraine. (see Figures 4.6 and 4.7).

So what could be relevant as content?

A corrie

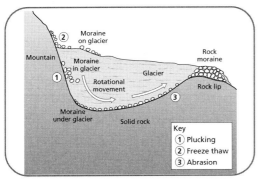

Diagram 4.6 Formation of a corrie

Key features

- ◆ Snow accumulates in a mountain hollow. Process is repeated over many, many years.
- ◆ Snow is compressed into ice, usually within north-facing hollows.
- ◆ Rotational movement, and ice moves downhill under gravity.
- ◆ Freeze-thaw weathering loosens rock above glacier.
- ◆ Plucking on backwall of corrie.
- ◆ Abrasion where moraine is dragged and erodes basin.
- ◆ Rock basin deepens at maximum point of erosion (over deepening).
- ◆ Ice melts and corrie loch left trapped by lip.

Terminal Moraine

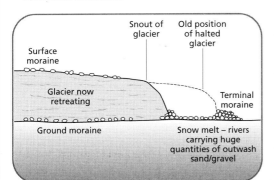

Figure 4.7 Formation of terminal moraine

Key features.

- ◆ Moraine is material first carried, then deposited by a glacier as it melts.
- ◆ Debris is pushed at the snout of the glacier.
- ◆ Made up of unsorted clay, sand and rocks.
- ◆ Extends across the glacial trough.
- ◆ Shows the maximum extent of the glacial advance.

Glacial features and OS maps

Map questions should be relatively straightforward. After all, the answer is on the map; all you have to do is recognise it. However you do need to know all the theory. Before you can recognise glaciated features from a map, you need to know what you are looking for. So the list of key features above is important. When you describe the features, you should always give grid references (4 or 6 as appropriate) and a location name if given. It is really not possible to recognise deposition features on a map. However you should be able to recognise the following erosion features: Corrie, corrie lochan, hanging valley, arête, glacial trough (U-shaped valley), ribbon lake, truncated spur, pyramidal peak, misfit stream.

Key Words and Definitions

Definition	Mass movement (or mass wasting) is the down slope movement of the regolith (i.e. loose soil, stones or rocks) by the force of gravity.

Key factors	Examples
Angle of slope	Generally the steeper the slope, the faster the movement.
Vegetation cover	Vegetation generally holds the soil/ rock in place.
Moisture in regolith	Water between soil particles generally allows sliding.
Rock structure	Slumping occurs in weaker soft soils.
Human activity	By deforestation, over grazing, quarrying and walking.
Time	Over time all landscapes change.

Mass Movement

Throughout the descriptions and explanations above, it is possible for the features to be changed (or modified) by mass movement.

Now check over your notes. The main mass movements relevant to our studies are scree slopes, rock falls, slumping and landslips.

Mass movements can have a human impact. For example, landslips can cause coastal cliffs to slump into the sea or block a railway line. In 1966, at Aberfan, Wales, a mudflow comprised of wet coal waste, slid into the village with deadly effects.

HOW TO PASS HIGHER GEOGRAPHY

Questions and Answers

SAQ 11 Draw an annotated diagram to describe and explain the conditions and processes which encourage one named mass movement. *(3 marks)*

Answer to SAQ 11

Scree (also known as talus; see Figure 4.8a) is the result of frost shattering (the most widespread form of physical weathering) and occurs in rocks that contain crevices and joints (for example carboniferous limestone, and some sedimentary rocks), where there is limited vegetation cover and variations in temperature. At night, water freezes in the cracks, and during the day temperatures rise and the ice melts. When repeated, the alternating freeze thaw action cause the rocks to shatter and come to rest at the foot of the rock face. This is a feature in both glaciated and mountain limestone areas.

Rockfalls are very rapid mass movements on steep slopes, caused by physical or chemical weathering in mountains or along sea cliffs. Material once separated from the surface will fall vertically to produce a scree slope or beach debris.

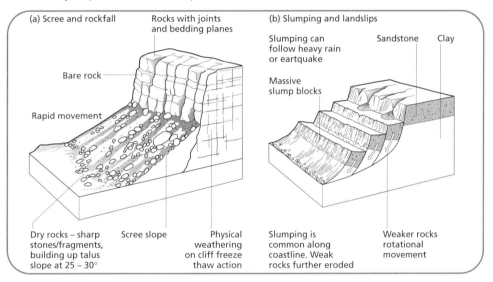

Figure 4.8a Scree and rockfall   **Figure 4.8b** Slumping and landslips

Slumping and landslips (see Figure 4.8b): A slump is a rotational movement often found in areas with clay or sandstone rocks, overlying more resistant or impermeable rocks (such as limestone or shale). A section of a slope can give way allowing a mass of unsupported, solid rock to slip or slide down. This mass movement is found along the southern and eastern coastal areas of England where the cliffs are often composed of soft glacial deposits and associated with retreating coastlines. (e.g. Lulworth Cove in Dorset). Can also follow a period of very heavy precipitation, or even triggered by earthquakes.

Mass movement questions will usually be tagged alongside a coastal, glaciated or mountain limestone question.

So there we have it. Another Environment Unit completed. Please note that much of this content can also appear as a question in the Interaction Unit, Rural Land Resources.

PHYSICAL ENVIRONMENT: BIOSPHERE CORE

What You Should Know

You should have a knowledge and understanding of:

◆ **Soils – properties and formation processes:**
◆ **Vegetation**

Remember this is written in the language of the SQA.

As you can see from the contents above, the Biosphere is essentially about soils and vegetation. Over the years I have found students, tend to find this core topic rather dull. Look for the logic which links the soil processes to the final soil type. Check through your soil notes.

Questions and Answers

SAQ 1   Try to complete a definition for each of the following terms. Match the words in column A with the range of definitions in Column B

Column A		Column B	
A	Ecosystem	1	a vertical section of the soil showing different layers or horizons
B	Podzol and podzolisation	2	a community of living plants and animals and the environment
C	Brown earth	3	leaching or capillary movement linked to water and temperature
D	Gley and gleying	4	the first plants to colonise an area
E	Horizon	5	acidic soils often in areas of cold coniferous forest or mountains
F	Nutrient movement	6	e.g. crumbly, blocky or platy, linked to the amount of water and air
G	Soil profile	7	how a soil or vegetation develops over time
H	Evolution	8	soils found in temperate deciduous forests
I	Succession	9	described by the content: % of sand, silt and clay

Questions and *Answers* continued ➤

Questions and Answers continued

Column A		Column B	
J	Climax vegetation	10	poorly drained soils and the processes involved
K	Pioneer	11	the different bands of soil making up a profile
L	Texture	12	the steady change of plants over time, e.g. weeds, small plants, shrubs and then trees
M	Structure	13	the final stage in succession. Balance reached between climate and soil

Answer SAQ 1

A2, B5, C8, D10, E11, F3, G1, H7, I12, J13, K4, L9, M6.

So what is soil?

Key Words and Definitions

Soil takes thousands of years to form, yet can be destroyed by abuse in a matter of a few years.

Soil is a mixture of weathered rock (minerals based on the broken-down bedrock – the regolith), (40%) decayed organic matter (10%) from leaves, roots, pine needles, dead biota (5%) (creepy crawlies!), air (22%) and water (23%).

Questions and Answers

SAQ 2   What are the main soil forming processes?

Answer to SAQ 2

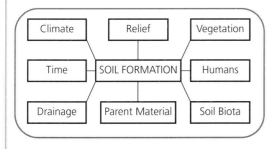

Figure 5.1 Factors affecting soil formation

Soil = parent material+ climate+ soil biota+ relief/ drainage+ time+ humans+ vegetation

Questions and Answers continued ➢

Questions *and* Answers *continued*

Answer to SAQ 2 continued

Parent Material   This is the main rock type, usually the bedrock (regolith), or sometimes glacial moraine. This affects soil in three main ways: the colour, the texture and the chemical composition of the soil. For example, red sandstone produces a red soil, 'sandy' in texture, while limestone and chalk produce alkaline soils.

Climate   Temperature and precipitation have a major influence upon the soil. High temperatures encourage vegetation and biota activity, while low temperatures discourage such action.

When the net movement of rainwater is downwards (i.e. when precipitation is greater than evaporation) this causes leaching and the removal of soluble minerals and humus. When evaporation is greater than precipitation, the net movement is upwards (called capillary action) and minerals are brought to the surface.

Vegetation   Vegetation has a major influence on the soil. Once again, this is a factor that is linked to climate and drainage. With dense vegetation you have plenty of litter and humus, and with warmth and moisture you can get a fertile soil.

Soil Biota   This includes all the creepy things and smelly things in the soil! (bacteria, worms, plants, roots, insects and so on). These organisms absorb nitrogen, mix and aerate the soil, hold the soil together and give it life. Decaying vegetation provides the humus needed for the topsoil, which is the fertile zone of the soil.

Relief and drainage   A slope allows water to run off or drain. Once the slope is steep, the chance of soil erosion increases. Flat land is usually poorly drained and the waterlogged surface does not permit a soil to form properly. Aspect, or direction of slope, also has an influence on the soil. South facing slopes are warmer than north-facing slopes. The heat encourages the presence and growth of vegetation and biota. Whether water can or cannot move through the soil easily will affect the development of the soil profile.

Time   Time is required for a soil to reach maturity. All of the above activities take many years to develop. When a glacier melts, the moraine will be no more than a jumbled heap of boulders, stones, particles and fine dust. It is reckoned that 10,000 years would be a reasonable time to pass before the soil becomes settled and mature.

Human activity   People increasingly appear to be able to hasten change. We clear woodlands, plant trees, grow crops, add chemicals and insecticides, burn moors and drain marshes.

Questions and Answers continued ➤

Questions and Answers *continued*

SAQ 3 Close this book, and then jot down the key words associated with each of the following soil process factors.

Parent Material; Climate; Soil Biota; Relief and drainage; Time; Vegetation

Answer to SAQ 3

Now check your answers against the notes above. How did you do?

What is a soil profile?

Key Words and Definitions

A soil profile is a vertical section through the soil showing its different horizons or layers.

Three idealised horizons exist in zonal soils.

Horizon A

Is the surface layer, the most productive layer, where biological activity and humus content are at their most active. It is the layer where surface litter and humus form and ferment, as well as the layer most affected by leaching

Horizon B

Also known as the subsoil. It is a zone of accumulation where clays and other materials are re-deposited.

Horizon C

This is the parent material, usually weathered rock (regolith) resting on the bedrock.

Introduction to the three case study soils

The three case study soils can all be found in the UK: the podzols, brown earths and gleys.

You need to know the details of these three soils. Check back through your course notes now. It is easier to try and work out a logical approach to the understanding of the formation of a podzol, a brown earth and a gley. If you understood the processes involved in soil formation above, then you can work out the logic. There is clearly a link between climate, relief and vegetation and consequently the resulting soil. You need to be able to recognise the main features of any one of the profiles, and you need to be able to draw any of the profiles. Start by looking at Figure 5.2 and the information below

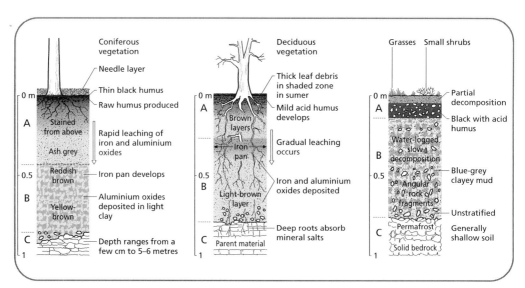

Figure 5.2 Soil profiles of a podzol, brown earth and a gley

	Podzol	Brown earth	Gley
Location	Northern coniferous forest or Taiga area of Europe.	Temperate deciduous forest of Central Europe, Russia, North America. Further south than Podzol.	Found is areas such as the permafrost outside the boundaries of the cold Tundra, or in any area with poor drainage, e.g. Dartmoor.
Relief and Drainage	Found on moorland, mountain sides and tops up to 250 or 350 metres.	Gently rolling land, hill sides, allowing the soil to be free draining.	Hollows and flat areas wet and exposed with poor drainage.
Climate	Long cool or cold winters and short mild to warm summers. Variable can be low to fairly heavy. Considerable snow.	Less extreme climatic conditions. Warmer conditions, lower precipitation, allowing more rapid decomposition. Favourable for vegetation growth.	Cold and wet. Although the rainfall could be high with waterlogging, a gley can also form in lower rainfall areas. The important factor is that there is little warmth on the soil.
Natural vegetation	Coniferous trees (e.g. pines, firs, spruces). Litter based on pines and needles.	Deciduous woodland, with trees such as ash, beech, oak. Litter based on plentiful leaf drop.	Vegetation growth is limited due to the lack of warmth and waterlogging. Adaptive species such as mosses, lichens and marsh vegetation.
Type of soil	Heavy with aluminium and iron, resulting in an acidic pedalfer soil. Strong profile with clear horizons.	Again a pedalfer soil. Horizons less distinct due to greater mixing. A milder, less acidic, slightly more alkaline soil.	Pedalfer again. But the effects of leaching and the lack of soil movement mean that you have a strong zonal soil.

	Podzol	Brown earth	Gley
Processes	Strong influence of climate, with lack of warmth and leaching of soil, (downward movement of iron, aluminium and humus). Formation of an iron pan. Climate also discourages biota. Few animals, worms or bacteria to mix and fertilise soil.	Far less negative influence of climate, with some warmth and gentler leaching of soil, (downward movement of iron, aluminium and humus). Iron pan may develop. Still a net downward movement of water.	The soil is deficient in oxygen, waterlogged, with little fresh litter being broken down very slowly in the wet conditions. Once again note that the soil is closely linked to climate and vegetation. All three work together.
Human response	Due to the climate, there is a short and limited growing season. Main use is commercial coniferous forest plantations. (However many such areas are remote, and over most of this zone the forest is untouched.) If you lime the soil, clear the vegetation, it would be possible to have limited cultivation based on oats, potatoes or hay. The iron pan restricts root penetration and waterlogging is a problem, especially after the spring snowmelt	Due to the longer, warmer summers and the amount of biota activity, animal action and litter, this soil has far greater fertility than the podzol. These areas carry a far greater population, and being closer to major cities, the land has been greatly cleared of its natural vegetation and replaced by agriculture. With the addition of manure and fertilisers, it is possible to grow grain crops, and graze cattle. The land also is suitable for housing, industry, and leisure. There are few barriers.	These areas have limited natural potential. You can have an influence on the soil by ploughing, manuring, applying lime and other fertilisers. The land can be drained. Only then could you keep sheep or low-value crops such as oats or potatoes.

Questions and Answers

SAQ 4   Identify the conditions (climate, relief and drainage) linked to each of the three soil types.   *(6 marks)*

Answer to SAQ 4

More detail will follow over the next page. However you can recognise the following:

Podzol   Found at higher altitudes (above 250 metres), increased precipitation, lower temperatures and length of growing season and where there is relatively free-flowing drainage due to a gentle slope.

Gley   Found at lower altitudes (below 100 metres), where there is less precipitation yet with waterlogged drainage conditions

Brown earth   Found between 100 and 250 metres, with generally free drainage, moderate length of growing season and moderate precipitation.

Questions and *Answers* continued ➤

Questions *and* Answers *continued*

SAQ 5   Choose one of the three soil types, and describe and explain the processes which have contributed to its formation.   *(5 marks)*

Answer to SAQ 5

Podzol

◆ Precipitation greater than evaporation leads to a downward movement of water and leaching.

◆ An iron/aluminium hardpan is formed creating a drainage barrier.

◆ Low temperatures result is low biota activity and a slow breakdown of litter.

◆ Acidic (mor) humus layer due to presence of pine needles and fir cones.

◆ Highly visible soil horizons.

Brown earth

◆ Precipitation slightly greater than evaporation leads to a downward movement of water and moderate leaching. May occasionally have a narrow hardpan.

◆ Faster decomposition due to warmer temperatures and less water. Lots of biota activity with action of worms, rodents, insects.

◆ Litter mainly from deciduous leaves, resulting in humus only slightly acidic.

◆ Highly visible soil horizons.

Gley

◆ Damp, waterlogged soils. Inadequate drainage. May show permafrost layer

◆ Horizons very poorly defined.

◆ Dark acidic (mor) humus from the slowly decomposed mosses, lichens and harsh vegetation.

◆ Very restricted biota action. Waterlogging and low temperatures do not encourage biological activity. Humus decays very slowly.

Analysis of soil profiles and data from soil surveys

There are two types of questions that could be asked under this SQA syllabus topic.

You could be given one or more profiles and asked to describe and then identify the soil type, giving your reasons (see SAQ 6), or you could be given a written description of a soil survey analysis and asked to identify the soil type, giving your reasons (see SAQ 7).

Questions and Answers

SAQ 6 For profiles A and B (Figure 5.3), describe and then identify each soil type, giving your reasons. *(6 marks)*

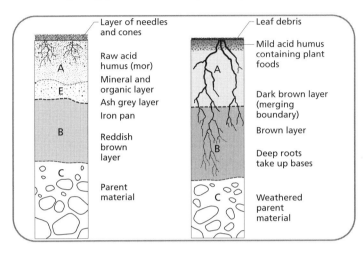

Diagram 5.3 Profiles A and B

Answer to SAQ 6

The order is important. First you describe the key features.

Profile A

There are clear layers

Evidence of leaching (minerals washed down and the presence of an iron pan).

Litter based on coniferous vegetation.

Presence of reddish-brown layer, is leached iron and aluminium.

Acidic soil is again expected from the pines and cones.

The presence of so much mor indicates limited biota activity.

That is the description, so now identify the soil type.

This description matches the conditions under which you get a podzol. Therefore that is the answer.

Profile B

Highly visible soil horizons.

Litter mainly from deciduous leaves, resulting in humus only slightly acidic.

Downward movement of water and moderate leaching.

More fertile soil with rich brown soil and good root depth.

Faster decomposition due to warmer temperatures and less water. Lots of biota activity, with action of worms, rodents, insects.

This description matches the conditions under which you get a brown forest soil. Therefore, that is the answer.

Questions and **Answers** continued ➤

Questions *and* Answers *continued*

SAQ 7 The following information was noted from a soil survey:

Location: Straiton, South Ayrshire
Altitude: 300 metres
Slope: 10 degrees
Vegetation: Mainly coniferous woodland, some clearings, rough grass
0–5 cms   Surface layer of needles and cones
                Acidic mor humus, pH 5.1
5–25 cms   Roots, minerals and more humus
25–35 cms   Ash grey mineral horizon
35–60 cms   Reddish-brown layer with iron pan
60 cms   Parent material

Using the information obtained from the soil survey analysis, identify the soil type, giving your reasons.   *(3 marks)*

Answer to SAQ 7

The answer to SAQ 7, is exactly the same as SAQ 6, Profile A.

Coastal Dunes

In a 'plant free' landscape, (e.g. after a landslide, or a lava flow, or a fresh sandy coastline, or derelict industrial wasteland) plants become established over a number of years and move from the pioneer phase through succession to a mature 'climax' community of stable vegetation.

The only such environment that will appear in the Higher Examination will be succession across a sand dune coast. Diagrams appear in all the books and several past Higher Papers. A coastal environment is a very harsh environment for plants to survive in. As you move inland, 200 metres or so from the high water mark, you pass through a number of zones. You need to be able to describe the zones, identify a number of the common plant species found, be able to describe how the physical conditions alter as you move inland and be able to explain why the plants have adapted to the subtle changes in the environment. What are the environmental changes that will occur as you move inland?

Sea ————————————————————➤ *Moving Inland*

Alkaline, becoming more neutral then acidic
Salinity (salt level) high becoming less so
Young transient sand dunes becoming mature and stable
Humus free then increasing in humus content
Lacking nutrients, then increasing nutrient level
No shelter from sea spray and winds, becoming sheltered
Salty seawater eventually becoming fresh water
Very dry, free draining sand becoming 'heavier' loam or clay soil
Very scant pioneer plant coverage becoming denser, moving to climax
Restricted vegetation variety becoming diverse

Questions and Answers

SAQ 8 'Plant succession describes the changes in vegetation that develop through time in a particular habitat'

a) Explain fully what is meant by 'climax vegetation'. *(3 marks)*

b) Study Figure 5.4, describe and explain the plant succession for a sand dune habitat. You should make reference to specific plants. *(6 marks)*

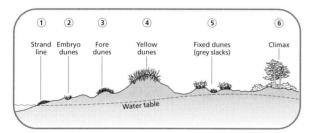

Figure 5.4 Successions across a sand dune coast

Answer to SAQ 8

a) You should be able to demonstrate an understanding of the process (called 'succession') that begins with pioneer species and moves through a number of phases to the final stage (climax). Over time plants reach an equilibrium state, and the vegetation cannot develop beyond that climax point. For example, in the environment described below the climax stage is mixed woodland of birch, pine alder or oak.

b) You need to describe the succession. You also need to check the information above. This summarises the physical changes you find as you move from stage 1 to stage 6. The vegetation found reflects the physical conditions found.

Stage 1 Strandline Seaweed and 'litter', sea sandwort, sea rocket, saltwort

The plants here are tolerant of the drying effects of the strings wind, sand, salt and spray. Shells add to the alkalinity. Lacking humus and nutrients.

Stage 2 Embryo Dune sand couch, lyme grass, sea rocket

A small 'baby' dune forms in the shelter behind the strand line. Often storm conditions destroy the embryo dune.

Stage 3 Fore Dune Sea holly, sand hedge, marram grass

Increase in humus and lower salt content allows a little more stability. Marram grass becomes increasingly a key plant in the build up of dunes.

Stage 4 Yellow Dune (main dune) marram grass, sand fescue, ragwort

Could now be 10 metres high. Continuing to build up the humus, nutrients and acidity levels. Less windy and more protected. Marram grass becomes the dominant plant. It has long tap- roots that are crucial in binding the soil together.

Questions and *Answers* continued ➤

Questions and Answers continued

Answer to SAQ 8 continued

Stage 5 Fixed Dunes (grey dunes and slacks) sand sedge, trefoil, buckthorn, heather, lichens

Plants that grow in more acidic conditions replace marram grass, requiring more shelter and a damper soil. Greater variety of plants develops. Damp hollows (slacks) form and water tolerant plants grow (reeds, willow and cotton grasses).

Stage 6 Climax heathland, machair, gorse, woodland (ash, alder, birch, spruce)

We have reached the end of the plant succession. The land here is likely to be damp, sheltered, acidic, rich in nutrients and humus.

As you can see the detail required for this question is fairly complex. What you need to concentrate on is the simple idea that the physical environment changes as you move away from the high water mark, and consequently the vegetation will change.

And finally, another question that can appear in the examination is one based on a diagram showing the results that could have been obtained by a field survey of a coastal sand dune transect.

Questions and Answers

SAQ 9 Study Figure 5.5 which shows information collected by students noting dominant vegetation while completing a survey at fixed distances from the sea.

Suggest reasons for the changes in vegetation along the line of transect. You should refer to the range of physical or environmental factors. *(6 marks)*

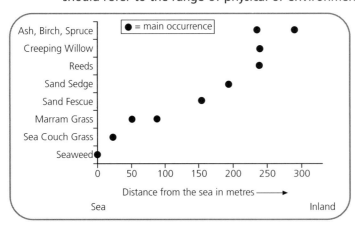

Figure 5.5 Survey of a coastal sand dune transect

Answer to SAQ 9

In fact the answer is really exactly the same as the answer for SAQ 8. Plants develop according to the physical conditions.

Well done! The biosphere topic is demanding. Concentrate on trying to understand the logical processes that result in soils and vegetation succession. Check back to the original SQA list of what you need to know.

HUMAN ENVIRONMENT: POPULATION CORE

Geography is also about people. This Core theme is about population numbers, population change and about the movement of people. You need to be able to describe data taken from tables, maps, graphs or population pyramids. Figure 6.1 shows the main issue, the growth in world population. Once again, a key theme throughout is that of change and the implications of such changes, whether they be with population movement (migration) or population structures. It is also important that you have a detailed knowledge of some case study examples.

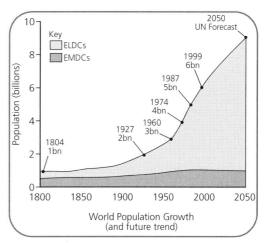

Figure 6.1 World population growth

Key Points

Demographic systems: Population change and migration

◆ You also need to be able to interpret population data from maps, in tables and diagrams, as well as from population pyramids.

Questions and Answers

SAQ 1 Demographic Systems

Some key definitions. Match column A with the appropriate explanation in column B

Column A		Column B	
A	Demography	1	Birth rate minus death rate
B	Birth rate	2	This is a total count of all the people living within an area or country

Questions and *Answers* continued ➤

Questions and Answers continued

SAQ 1 *continued*

Column A		Column B	
C	Death rate	3	This is a calculation based on the formula:–

$$\text{dependency ratio} = \frac{\text{(Children (0-14) + The Aged (65+)}}{\text{Adults (15–64)}}.$$

Column A		Column B	
D	General fertility	4	The average life span (in years) of the population of an area or country.
E	Infant mortality	5	The name given to the study of populations.
F	Life expectancy	6	The number of babies born in a year per thousand people in that area.
G	Dependency ratio	7	The rate which expresses the number of live births per 1000 women, aged 15–44, in a year.
H	Population census	8	The number of infant deaths (under 1 year old) in a year for every thousand babies born.
I	Natural increase	9	The number of deaths in a year per thousand people in that area.
J	Migration	10	Basic definition is the movement of people. For practical purposes it usually involves a change of home for a period of time.

Answer to SAQ 1

A-5, B-6, C-9, D-7, E-8, F-4, G-3, H-2, I-1, J-10

Useful sites: www.prb.org, www.measurecommunication.org, www.popnet.org

The Gathering of Population Data

Questions and Answers

SAQ 2 What is a census and why do we have one?

Questions and *Answers* continued ➤

Questions and Answers continued

Answer to SAQ 2

Since 1801, every 10 years the UK has set aside one day for the Census – a count of all people and households. It is the most complete source of information about the population that we have. The latest Census was held on Sunday, 29 April 2001.

It is the only survey which provides a detailed picture of the entire population.

The information the Census provides allows central and local government, health authorities and many other organisations to target their resources more effectively and to plan housing, education, health and transport services for years to come.

We all use public services at various times – including schools, health services, roads and libraries. These services need to be planned, and in such a way that they keep pace with fast-changing patterns of modern life. We need accurate information on the numbers of people, where they live and what their needs are. While this is true for a EMDC, it is also true for ELDCs. Every 10 years the Census provides a benchmark. Uniquely, it gives us a complete picture of the nation. It counts the numbers of people living in each city, town and country area. It tells us about each area and its population, including the balance of young and old, what jobs people do and the type of housing they live in.

The Census costs some £255 million for the UK as a whole, but the information it provides enables billions of pounds of taxpayers' money to be targeted where it is needed most. The Census gives us invaluable facts about:

Source: www.statistics.gov.uk/census2001/www.gro-scotland.gov.uk/ www.statistics.gov.uk. Check out the Internet sites.

In the UK there is also a legal requirement to record 'vital events' – births, marriages and deaths. This data is a useful way of monitoring population change at local, regional and national levels. In Scotland the Register General of Scotland supervises this. The Government and individual departments, the European Union and many other organisations all collect data. Surveys and questionnaires allow every aspect of our lives to be recorded. We are certainly not short of data!

Questions and Answers

SAQ 3 Using named examples, explain why ELDCs may find the collection of population data

(a) more difficult and (b) less reliable than EMDCs. *(5 marks)*

The UK census is very accurate. So what happens in the less economically developed world?

Questions and Answers continued ➤

HOW TO PASS HIGHER GEOGRAPHY

Questions *and* Answers *continued*

If it is important to allocate resources wisely in a rich country, then it is even more vital to use limited resources in a poorer country. However there are sometimes real difficulties in getting accurate data:

◆ High costs of conducting a census (e.g. in India, possibly as high as £1 billion!).

◆ Low level of adult literacy (e.g. Sierra Leone at 16%) and sometimes many language within a country.

◆ The sheer size and number of people (e.g. China, with over 1.2 billion people and 1 million villages.)

◆ War, ethnic tensions and political rivalries (e.g. Afghanistan, Kosovo, Iraq).

◆ Suspicion from local people (e.g. rural areas in Yemen or in the shanty towns of Calcutta).

◆ Costs of training enumerators (e.g. China required over 1 million people to organise the 2000 census).

◆ Poor communication and remoteness (e.g. Papua New Guinea/Brazil).

◆ Migration within countries and rapid movement to the cities (e.g. Mexico and Mexico City).

 An example source: China Population Information link www.cpirc.org.cn/eindex.htm

Population pyramids

The structure of a population depends upon birth and death rates as well as in and out migration. It is best shown using a **population pyramid**. This shows population according to age and gender at a particular time. You can use pyramids to study the population of one country at a particular time or compare different countries. You can also detect the impact of events such as migration, war, famine, population control programmes or even mass vaccination campaigns.

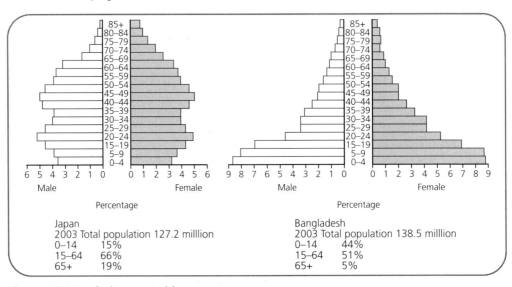

Figure 6.2 Population pyramids

Questions and Answers

SAQ 4 a) With reference to Figure 6.2, describe the main features of both pyramids. (Pyramid A, Japan and pyramid B, Bangladesh). *(3 marks)*

b) Account for (explain) the main features. *(6 marks)*

Answer to SAQ 4

a) **Pyramid A.** EMDCs. You should recognise 3 stages: children, adults and the aged. You can also use a (limited) number of stats from the pyramids. The narrow base indicates a low number of children (usually a falling fertility), with fewer than 20% of the population under 15. The bullet-shaped pyramid shows over 60% of the population in the adult stage (15–64). There is an increasing number of aged (65+) rising to over 20% of the population. Usually there are more older women than men.

Pyramid B. ELDCs. The broad-based pyramid indicates a youthful population with over 40 % of the population under 15 years. The tapering pyramid shows a rapid decline in the number of adults. The very narrow peak indicates that no more than 5% of the population is over 65. There are usually slightly more older men than women.

Some comments on Japan

15 September is 'Respect the Aged Day'! There are now 21,000 centenarians in Japan (86% are women). The healthiest area is the island group, Okinawa. Research suggests that this is due to their healthy diet (fish, seaweed, soya, vegetables) climate, close knit community, exercise and low stress lifestyle.

b) An explanation of population change (explanations mostly involve changes to fertility and mortality rates)

Factors affecting fertility

Birth rates can increase when: children are viewed as economic assets to work on a farm (Bangladesh) or as labour in factories (Philippines); are used to look after parents as they get older (Mali); when seen as an indicator of virility and as a status symbol (Mexico); (esp. male) continue the family name (Korea). Religious influences encourage fertility (as in Islam or Roman Catholicism). Fertility seems to be higher when women have less status in a society (Pakistan); in rural areas, when early marriage is encouraged (Burkina Faso); where there is poverty (Senegal). Rates are high when there is high infant mortality (Ethiopia), where there is little birth control (Niger).

Birth rate and fertility rates drop when infant mortality rates drop (Jordan); schooling becomes compulsory (esp. for girls) and women achieve increasing equality and status (Tunisia); when there is increasing affluence with economic growth (South Korea); later marriage (China) and the costs of raising children become an issue (USA); with widespread, and acceptability of, birth control (Iran); with improving health programmes (India); with government policies introduced to encourage parents to consider smaller families (China).

Overall, there is not a country in the world, that has not experienced a drop in birth rates over the last 30 years.

Questions and *Answers continued* ➤

Factors affecting mortality

Mortality rates increase or remain high where there is poverty (Bangladesh), famine (Ethiopia), war (Afghanistan), disease (Botswana), drought (NE Brazil), out migration of the young, overcrowding (Calcutta, India) and poor housing (esp. in shanty towns), poor diet and lack of medical care (Zimbabwe).

Mortality rates decrease and life expectancy increases when public health measures are present (clean water, health care) there is sufficient food and increasing wealth, and a reduction of childhood and other diseases (by vaccination and medical advances). Overall, there is scarcely a country in the world, that has not experienced a drop in death or mortality rates over the last 30 years.

An assessment of the impact of these changes

Questions *and* **Answers**

SAQ 5 With reference to at least one named country, what are the consequences of rapid population growth in ELDCs?   *(4 marks)*

Answer to SAQ 5

Make sure you refer to at least one or two countries or regions within the ELD world.

- ◆ With so many children, there is pressure on the provision of child health care, primary and secondary education, neo- and post-natal facilities. (e.g. Ethiopia, Chad, Mali).
- ◆ Such a youthful population will in turn become adults and a 'population momentum' will build up.
- ◆ The high proportion of 'dependents' will put a strain on the relatively low number of workers.
- ◆ There will also be the possibility of food shortages leading to malnutrition and possible famine.
- ◆ There will be a continuing problem of housing shortages/overcrowding/unemployment (Mexico).
- ◆ It will be very difficult to solve the basic problem facing many of the ELDCs with a population that is consuming all the resources. That basic problem is **poverty**.

Of course this could all be considered negative. There are many countries that believe that a growing population is healthy and that it contains the future of that country. The scare of population growth is 'propaganda fuelled by the rich world' in an attempt to keep the poorer countries poor. You decide!

Questions and **Answers** *continued* ➤

PHYSICAL ENVIRONMENT: ATMOSPHERE CORE

Questions and Answers continued

SAQ 6 With reference to at least one named country, what are the consequences of an increasingly aged population in an EMDC? *(4 marks)*

Answer to SAQ 6

When a person retires at 60 he/she may well have 25 years of life left. Such people may have worked for 40 years and most certainly have earned the support that some of the aged may require.

However, take as an example, Japan or Scotland

- ◆ With so many aged people, it is recognised that there will be a need for greater provision for geriatric care, with extra costs for the government and local authorities

- ◆ With more aged 'dependents', there is more of a burden on the working population to provide the wealth.

- ◆ Probable need to raise retirement age or increase taxes, leading to unhappiness for the working population.

- ◆ Less demand for other services, with closures or scaled down primary schools, nursery schools and maternity units

- ◆ Possible future shortage of people of working age.

Of course many of the young people reading this section well not be happy with some of these implications. It may be that a solution to some of these issues would be to increase in-migration of people of working age. Also you may have to work longer and retire later, and pay more in taxes to pay for your pension! You may also be encouraged to have more children.

Example

A case study example   AIDS   Zambia

Implication of population change caused by AIDS.

It is always difficult to get up-to-date non-sensationalist information about AIDS (Acquired Immune Deficiency Syndrome) and its impact. I went 'on line', punched in the words 'AIDS and Zambia'. I got hundreds of hits. However it is important to make sure that the information given is fair, correct and unbiased. Be careful. 19% of the population of Zambia has HIV and that will eventually result in death from AIDS. Poverty creates an environment that ensures the virus is spread. Poverty also hastens death among AIDS sufferers as a poor diet will increase the likelihood of catching diseases that the body's immune system can no longer deal with. Whereas in the past it was the weakest who died, usually the very young and the old, with AIDS it is different. It kills young adults, the producers of wealth, the workers, farmers and parents. In the absence of state welfare payments, and with the

Example continued ➤

Example *continued*

limited amount of help from charities, the burden of bringing up these orphans falls on to the extended family. This puts pressure on resources. For the future, the implications of the AIDS epidemic are very serious. The demands upon the health and education services for the country's scarce resources will be great. People's earning capacity and spending may also fall. Apart from the economic issues there is also massive social and human distress.

The Demographic Transition Model

A model in Geography is a diagram, graph, flow diagram or sketch that shows the key features of the subject. The Demographic Transition Model (DTM) was first proposed in the 1940s and describes the stages in the relationship between birth and death rates, and overall population changes. The model is positive and hopeful since it does suggest that in time mortality and fertility will decline as a result of social and economic development. It predicts that all countries will eventually reach stage 4 of the DTM.

You should now revise your notes on the model.

Questions and Answers

SAQ 7   Draw the main features of the model. Give each of the four stages a name and briefly describe the key features of birth and death rates in each stage.   *(6 marks)*

Answer to SAQ 7

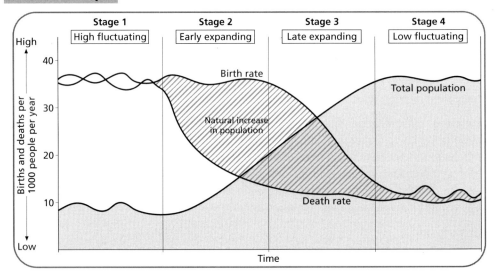

Figure 6.3 Stages in the Demographic Transition Model

Questions and *Answers* continued ➤

Questions and Answers continued

Answer to SAQ 7 continued

Stage	1	2	3	4
Examples	UK pre 1750 Remote native groups (e.g. rainforest)	UK 1750 – 1880 Zambia, Peru, Gambia	UK 1880 – 1940 China, India, Cuba	Post 1940 Japan, Germany, Italy

Stage 1 Birth rates and death rates flutuate at a high level (about 35 per 1000) giving a small population growth

Birth rates are high because:
• No birth control or family planning
• So many children die in infancy that parents tend to produce more in the hope that several will live
• Many children are needed to work on the land
• Children are regarded as a sign of virility
• Religious beliefs (e.g. Roman Catholics, Muslims and Hindus) encourage large families

High death rates, especially among children, are due to:
• Disease and plague (bubonic, cholera, kwashiorkor)
• Famine, uncertain food supplies, poor diet
• Poor hygiene – no piped, clean water and no sewage disposal
• Little medical science – few doctors, hospitals, drugs

Stage 2 Birth rates remain high, but death rates fall rapidly to about 20 per 1000 people giving a rapid population growth

The fall in death rates result from:
• Improved medical care – vaccinations, hospitals, doctors, new drugs and scientific inventions (e.g. Kenya)
• Improved sanitation and water supply
• Improvements in food production, both quality and quantity (e.g. Pakistan)
• Improved transport to move food, doctors
• A decrease in child mortality

Stage 3 Birth rates now fall rapidly, to perhaps 20 per 1000 people, while death rates continue to fall slightly (15 per 1000 people), to give a slowly increasing population

The fall in birth rate may be due to:
• Family planning – contraceptives, sterilisation, abortion and government incentives (e.g. 1 child policy – China)
• A lower infant mortality rate meaning less pressure to have so many children
• Increased industrialisations and mechanisation meaning fewer labourers are needed (e.g. India)
• Increased desire for material possessions (cars, holidays, bigger homes) and less for large families
• An increased incentive for smaller families – healthier children
• Emancipation of women, enabling them to follow their own careers rather than being solely child bearers (e.g. Portugal)

Stage 4 Both birth rates (12 per 1000) and death rates (10 per 1000) remain low, fluctuating slightly to give a limited population change. Indeed in some countries, population may be in decline (e.g. Scotland)

Figure 6.3 continued

A good model in social science always has the scope to change and adapt with the times. Can there be a stage 5? This would be when birth rates fall below that of death rates. That has already happened in a number of European countries (for example Scotland!). Will this lead to a declining population? Possibly. It is too early to state with certainty that this is a new stage or a phase of stage 4. You decide!

Let's have a look at a sample of the DTM questions that have appeared over the years.

SAQ 8 Chose one of the stages of the Demographic Transition Model. Describe and explain the features that affect population growth at that stage. You should refer to at least one named country. *(4 marks)*

Or

SAQ 9 Describe the changes that have taken place in either the birth or death rate line through stages 1–4. You should refer to at least one named country. *(3 marks)*

Or

SAQ 10 Describe and explain those factors which bring about a change in either birth or death rates. You should refer to at least one named country. *(4 marks)*

Or

SAQ 11 Referring to a country or countries which you have studied, describe and account for the changes in population from the beginning of stage 2 to the end of stage 3. *(8 marks)*

Questions and Answers continued ➤

Questions and Answers continued

There you have it: four questions, similar in some respects.

Just to vary it a little bit, let's have a look at a genuine student answer and analyse it.

Student answer to SAQ 9

I am going to look at changes in the birth rate. In stage 1 the birth rate is high (½) at over 33 per 1000 (½). It remains high throughout stage 2 (½). By stage 3 the rate starts to drop rapidly down (½) to about 14 per 1,000 (½). The final stage sees the rate staying low (½) but gently swinging up and down (½).

Apart from one flaw this answer was fine. The changes have been noted, and the student has given some of the actual birth rates. Have you noted the flaw? There is no mention of any country. Counting up the half marks, this candidate got more than full marks, but the markers were instructed that if there was no mention of a country, to mark out of a maximum of 2½.

Answer to SAQ 11

Stage 2

You could take as your example country/ countries the UK during the 19th century or ELDCs such as Bangladesh or Ethiopia. Change was due to a high birth rate and a falling death rate, resulting in an increased growth rate. (For full reasons see notes above.)

Some reasons for high birth rate (again link the reasons to your selected country):

◆ Lack of birth control/ family planning due to religious, cultural, and 'traditional' views.

◆ High infant mortality rate, due to food shortages, diseases, poverty, poor housing.

◆ Parents wanting to have many children as an 'insurance policy'.

◆ Children seen as an 'economic' asset. In many ELDCs children should be viewed as an 'extra pair of hands' for work rather than an 'extra mouth' to feed.

◆ In a poor country children are viewed a genuine source of joy in an otherwise bleak existence.

◆ Religious beliefs and attitudes encourage large families.

Some reasons for the drop in death rates:

◆ Many improvements in medical care (drugs, education, doctors, hospitals, vaccinations).

◆ Public health projects in sanitation and water supply.

◆ Increased food production and better diets.

◆ Children now living longer with a drop in infant mortality rates.

Stage 3

You could take as your example country, the UK during the early part of the 20th century to 1940, or ELDCs such as India or China. Changes were due to a falling birth rate and a gentle drop in death rates, resulting in a slowing down of the growth rate (for full reasons see notes above).

Questions and *Answers* continued ➤

Questions *and* Answers *continued*

Answer to SAQ 11 continued

Some reasons to explain drop in birth rates:

◆ Family planning (contraceptives, sterilisation, abortion and government incentives and initiatives).
◆ A lower infant mortality rate meaning less pressure to have as many children.
◆ Increased industrialisation, resulting in a need for fewer labourers.
◆ Children becoming more of an 'economic liability' rather than an 'asset'.

Some reasons for the continuing drop in death rates:

Same reasons as above. Obviously the rate of decrease is now slowing down. We continue to make progress in medical matters, food supply and public health.

Example

Case Study China's Population Policy

China hit the 1.3 billion mark during the year 2000, meaning that about 22% of the world's population lived in this one country! For over 25 years the Chinese have adopted a population policy that encourages (and some would say coerces) a strict limit on the number of children being born into a family. In 1979 the 'one child' family policy was imposed. China's economic growth was being eroded and devalued by the spectacular growth in population. Death rates had dropped and with birth rates lagging behind, China saw an explosion in population. (Between 1962 and 1973, the population grew by 35% from 660 million to 900 million). See notes for stages 2 and 3 in the Demographic Transition Model. A drastic problem needed a drastic solution! Some of the key components of the policy:

◆ Permission had to be given by local groups to allow couples to marry.
◆ Late marriage enforced.
◆ Permission required to 'try' for a baby.
◆ For those who followed the policy, there was priority in education, housing, pensions, health care, food and clothing rations and ownership of land. (Such inducements were removed with the birth of a second child).
◆ There were massive social pressure to comply, with public denouncement of those who failed to comply.
◆ There was massive resources put into health and family planning clinics, with contraception, abortion and sterilisation available.

There was resistance from many groups, especially in the rural areas, where children were still required to work the land. It should also be noted that there are massive human rights issues linked to such a policy. China's population would be 1.6 billion if this policy had not been introduced in 1979. The policy has been relaxed in recent years and in most rural areas a second child will be allowed, subject to local approval. Some concern has been stated regarding the 65 million 'little emperors/ empresses'. This is the name given to the single children, stereotyped as being spoiled and pampered. Finally there is a notable imbalance between the ratios of boy/girl babies. For every 100 girls born there are 115 boys.

You may wish to check out some theories on the internet to explain this.

Migration

Remind yourself of what SQA requires you to know about migration

Questions and Answers

SAQ 12 Define and give named examples of each of the following types of migration: Permanent, Temporary, Voluntary, Forced, International, Intra-national. *(6 marks)*

Answer to SAQ 12

Types of migration: migration can be temporary or permanent, voluntary or forced, international or internal. Migrants can also be labelled according to the reason for their move: e.g. as asylum seekers, or economic migrants or refugees.

Temporary:

Daily e.g. commuting daily from Auchterarder to Glasgow for work.

Seasonal e.g. a two-week holiday in Majorca or herders in the Sinai Desert, Egypt.

Contract (job-related): e.g. working for a British bank in Switzerland for a fixed period.

Other e.g. a student taking a year out to do voluntary work in Bolivia, or a 'guest 'worker in a country (e.g. Saudi Arabia) intending to return home (Pakistan) at some stage.

Sometimes the word 'circulation' is used, since the intention is that the person will return to the original point. When there is no such plan then migration will be

Permanent:

e.g. a retired couple leaving Scotland to live in Mediterranean Spain, or a family moving to a bigger house in Glasgow, or rural people leaving the Ganges Valley to live in a large city.

Voluntary:

When people have been free to move and the barriers or obstacles have been easily overcome. Usually such movements are linked to a search for an improved quality of life, and people have made a free choice: e.g, a young couple in Scotland moving to Australia to 'start a new life'.

Forced:

When people feel they have no choice, they move because they have to, and more often than not such migrations involve suffering and a lower quality of life.

International:

Involves the crossing of national boundaries, e.g. from Turkey into Germany or from Mexico into the USA.

Internal or intra-national:

occurs within a country or even within a city.

Questions and **Answers** continued ➤

Questions *and* **Answers** *continued*

Answer to SAQ 12 continued

urban to urban: e.g. simply moving house within or between towns

urban to rural: e.g. moving out of Glasgow or London to the countryside

rural to urban: e.g. from the countryside in China to one of the big cities.

An **asylum seeker** is a person who feels threatened in their home country and who declares him/herself as such when they arrive at a 'host' country. The cause can be religious or ethnic persecution, and the seeker is in real danger of imprisonment or death if they return. (This could be a migrant into the UK from Iran or Iraq or Afghanistan.)

An **economic migrant** is the term used to describe a person who has moved to improve the quality of life and earn more money for themselves and possibly their families. Examples would include Scots going to Canada or Indian migrant coming to the UK.

A **refugee** is a stateless person who finds him/herself displaced and homeless. This may follow war, famine, religious or ethnic persecution. A refugee is usually without documents or belongings.

Why do people migrate? What are the causes of migration?

You need to be able to recognise the basic factors that break down into push factors, those negative features of the old location, (origin) which encourage people to leave that area, and pull factors, those positive features or attractions of the new location (destination). Sometimes the pull factors are no more than a 'dream'.

Questions *and* **Answers**

SAQ 13   Organise the following list into push and pull factors. You should note that often a pull factor is the exact opposite of a push factor. E.g. lack of educational opportunities (push) and good educational opportunities (pull).

Lack of basic amenities   pollution   educational provision   overcrowding low wages war   unemployment   high mortality rates   poor housing good housing   poverty   good hospitals   few doctors   natural hazards loss of farmland   lack of land   crime   population growth   famine or drought   religious bigotry   ethnic confrontation   low standard of living social amenities (clubs and cinemas)   political stability

Questions *and* **Answers** *continued* ➤

Questions and Answers continued

SAQ 14 With reference to an example of a population migration between two named countries:

a) Explain the migration in terms of 'push' and 'pull' factors, and *(4 marks)*

b) Discuss the advantage and disadvantages which the migration has brought to

i. The 'losing' country (origin), and *(4 marks)*

ii. The 'receiving' country (host) *(4 marks)*

Answer to SAQ 14

Case Study

India to the UK, an example of voluntary, international permanent migration

Host Country, UK

Pull factors

Commonwealth link, higher wages, high standard of living, job prospects, education and health services.

Benefits of migration to the UK

Enrichment of UK culture e.g. music, fashion and food; fits in well with UK society labour needs: e.g. skilled workers in health, less skilled in textiles; creative and enterprising people.

Problems encountered in the UK

Illogical discrimination in the host country. Treated as scapegoats for all UK problems, such as unemployment, falling service standards in housing, education and health. Differences in language, religion and clash of cultures.

Country of origin, India

Push factors

Rural poverty, unemployment lowers quality of life, especially in health, housing and education. The caste system, religious clashes and loss of farmland.

Benefits of migration to India

Reduced local unemployment, reduced crowding on the land and pressure on limited health, educational and housing resources. Workers often send money home to India, creating some additional wealth.

Problems encountered in India

There is a loss of the more dynamic, young, and enterprising workforce and the population left may be imbalanced with too few men.

Another good and popular answer to this type of question will be the 'voluntary' migration from Turkey into West Germany in the 1960s and 1970s. This study is also well documented in the Higher Geography books. Look at the following question.

A migration model

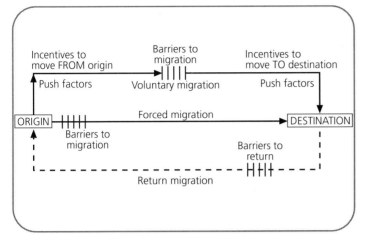

Figure 6.4 Migration model

Questions and Answers

SAQ 15 Study the migration model (Figure 6.4)

a) Describe what the model is showing *(3 marks)*

b) Referring to one named example of each type of migration, voluntary and forced, explain why the migration took place. *(5 marks)*

c) What obstacles have to be overcome? *(2 marks)*

d) What reasons could there be for return to the original country? *(2 marks)*

Answer to SAQ 15

a) With models you always need a point to start, I would suggest the left hand side at the origin. So how do you move to the destination? There are two routes, both with barriers. The routes 'forced ' and 'voluntary' are defined above. Voluntary migrations (for example Turkey to West Germany) take place when there are incentives to move from (push) the origin and incentives to move to (pull) the destination. The diagram also shows that a return route is possible. Whichever route is taken there are barriers to be overcome.

b) **Case study 1 Central Turkey to West Germany** (1960s, 1970s and 1980s), a voluntary migration

Your answer should be structured around 'push' and 'pull' factors

Push Factors

◆ Central area in Turkey is very poor and isolated

◆ Local economy based on traditional farming

Questions and Answers continued ➤

Questions and Answers continued

Answer to SAQ 15 continued

- Region has few natural resources
- Limited schooling, health and housing
- Population growth resulted in unemployment
- Few opportunities to earn money, wages low
- Increased mechanisation added to unemployment
- Low quality of living
- Political insecurity
- Area is an active earthquake zone

Pull Factors

- Initial demand was for farmers
- Demand for labour to rebuild German economy
- Demand for labour to take the jobs that Germans considered to be too dirty or poorly paid, e.g. car factories.
- Attraction of high wages
- Attraction of a better way of life
- Promise of education and training
- Political security
- Possibility of saving money

c) Obstacles

There are several barriers that can hold back people from migrating across international borders.

There is the cost of transport and setting up home in another country, the distances involved can be a psychological barrier and government restrictions (both on leaving and entering another country) such as quota limits and work permits. Other obstacles could be a lack of skills, a lack of information and lack of awareness of opportunities, language and religious barriers and the trauma of leaving a family behind.

d) Return

The model does provide a route for return to the original country. This is not always possible once the ties have been broken. For many migrants the move has been successful and a new life established. However migration does not always work, and the reality of the move may not have led to the opportunities imagined. In other words, the 'pull' factors were not realised. Another factor may be that the cause for migration has been removed. (e.g. Iraqi migrants can possibly return home since the Saddam Hussein regime has been overthrown). It could also be that there were racial, cultural, language and religious tensions. However some migrants return because they miss their family or simply because they have earned enough money to start a business back home.

HUMAN ENVIRONMENT: RURAL GEOGRAPHY

Agriculture over the last few years has featured regularly in our newspapers and on TV. Why should this be so? We have been concerned with 'foot and mouth', 'mad cow' disease, genetically modified (GM) food, the growing use of pesticides and fertilisers, loss of farmland and so on. Farming is now front-page news, so read your papers and keep up to date!

What You Should Know

◆ Agricultural systems
◆ Rural landscapes
◆ Rural changes (since 1950)

You should now gather together your Rural Geography notes and read them.

In some ways the structure of this unit is similar to that of the Industry Core, with an emphasis on **Systems, Landscapes and Change**.

Questions and Answers

SAQ 1   Define each of these terms.

★ **Subsistence**   ★ **Shifting**   ★ **Pastoralism**   ★ **Peasant**   ★ **Low technology**
★ **Extensive**   ★ **Commercial**   ★ **Sedentary**   ★ **Arable**   ★ **Advanced**
★ **High technology**   ★ **Intensive**

Answer to SAQ 1

Subsistence	Producing crops for own family use, nothing available to sell
Commercial	Large-scale farming for selling on the market for profit
Shifting	When farmers move on a regular pattern from place to place
Sedentary	Where farmers remain fixed in a place, and fields are farmed year after year
Pastoralism	Where the main farming effort is put into rearing and looking after animals
Arable	Where the main farming effort is put into growing (grain) crops, e.g. wheat

Questions and *Answers* continued ➤

Questions *and* Answers *continued*

Answer to SAQ 1 continued

Peasant	Basic and traditional farming methods used
Advanced	Modern methods and systems relying on a business approach
Low technology	Relying on hand labour and low levels of scientific assistance
High technology	Using all the modern and high-tech systems, machines and science
Extensive	Farming over a large area, with low output per hectare
Intensive	Farming with a high output per hectare, usually requiring lots of labour, money and machines.

So how did you get on? When we introduce the three farming systems, you should be able to apply these words.

The Farming System

Whatever the agriculture system in the world, you can split it into *inputs* (physical and human), *processes and outputs*.

Questions *and* Answers

SAQ 2   Complete the three boxes below by placing the key words in the correct column.

Inputs (Physical/Human)   **Processes**   **Outputs**

Key words

Livestock, sowing, altitude, transport, eggs, fodder, harvesting, wind, ploughing, capital, slope, crops, fertilising, milk, vegetables, market, government policy, temperature, soils, rainfall. (See if you can add a few examples yourself.)

Answer to SAQ 2

Physical Inputs	Human Inputs	Processes	Outputs
altitude	transport	ploughing	livestock
wind	capital	harvesting	eggs
slope	government policy	sowing	fodder crops
temperature	market	fertilising	milk
rainfall	farm size		vegetables
soils			arable crops

One of the questions you could be asked to do, is to 'annotate and analyse field sketches and photographs of rural landscapes.'

So what do you do? First note the number of marks. Remember that 1 correct point equates to a half mark. If the question is for 3 marks, go for 6 points and a couple of extra points for luck! Always state the obvious and draw attention to what you see and what you would expect to see on the sketch.

Commercial Arable Farming

Farming System 1

Study the annotated photograph below.

Oh, if it was this easy in the final exam! Remember that you may be asked to annotate a photo or sketch in the exam. You should write as much as you can. Remember that you get a half mark for each correct point.

Low population density   Prairie landscape   Lack of hedgerows/field boundaries

Grain crops wheat, barley

High output per worker

Extensive use of machinery

Flat featureless landscape

Extensive farming

Linear road pattern

Fertile chernozem soil

Shelter belt trees

Scattered settlement   Large rectangular fields   Isolated buildings

Figure 7.1 Commercial Arable Farming

Questions and Answers

SAQ 3 Using the photograph of commercial arable farming (Figure 7.1), or any similar named area, describe the main features of the landscape. *(3 marks)*

Describe the farming inputs and outputs and farming methods in such an area, and explain the changes that have taken place since the 1950s. *(6 marks)*

Questions and Answers continued ➤

Questions and Answers continued

Summary Notes

Location   Prairies of North America, e.g. Saskatchewan, North and South Dakota, eastern England (East Anglia)

Key Words   Commercial, sedentary, arable, advanced, high technology, extensive and high output per worker

Settlement   Low population density and scattered settlement. Limited employment opportunities. Originally large areas of cheap land. Planned out in regular grid iron sectors. Areas often remote and isolated. Settlements reflect historical development in late 19th and early 20th centuries. Linear settlements alongside straight roads and railways, a planned landscape, which grew in a hierarchical pattern with a network of small farms, small towns and occasionally a large service centre town. Following amalgamation of farms, many farmhouses now abandoned. Land is cheap.

Methods   Climatic inputs favour grain farming with warm sunny summers, low precipitation (summer maximum) with cold winters. Labour input low but output per worker high due to the massive investment in machinery which controls ploughing, fertilising and harvesting. Contract workers on farms.

Landscape   Dominated by high-technology machines, with few but skilled workers. Large areas of land producing low output/hectare, allowing large fields to be cultivated using machinery. Irrigation used in selected areas. Soils can be fertile (Chernozems), but climate makes farming often marginal. Large rectangular fields with a landscape of straight roads and railways. Grain crops dominate (wheat, barley) with other crops growing in importance (sunflowers, oilseed rape). Land often flat and featureless. Use of contract labour. Crops stored in silos. Importance of railways to transport output. Lack of hedgerows/boundaries

Concerns   Farms often owned by large businesses. Climatic patterns seem to be changing, resulting in far more extreme conditions. Problems with hail and early frost. Growing concern with soil erosion (flat featureless fields).

Modern scientific approach has given concern about chemical pollution of the land. Often the hedges are being cut back, with the land now becoming expensive. With world overproduction in certain crops, quotas introduced. There is rural depopulation and an abandonment of homesteads and collapse of services. There is a movement to increase the range of crops grown.

Shifting Cultivation

Farming System 2

Summary Notes

Location	Tropical rainforest zones of South America, Africa, SE Asia (e.g. Boro Indians of the Amazon)
Key Words	Subsistence, Shifting, Peasant/Traditional, Low Technology, Extensive, Low output/ worker
Settlement	300 million people worldwide living in low population density (10 hectares required to support one person) due to isolation, climate, dense forest, infertile land cannot support more people, disease. Settlement is dispersed, with small clearings (chagras) with community houses (malocas).
Methods	Clearings created using 'slash and burn' techniques. Machetes used to cut down vegetation, which is then burnt. Ash used as fertiliser. Crops such as manioc, maize, yams and cassava planted using basic stick tools. Heavy rains cause soils to be leached, washing out fertility. Clearings abandoned (every 4 or so years) and left to regenerate (40 years) Battling against encroaching weeds. Process starts again, with new clearing.
Landscape	Largest trees and fruit trees left in position. There is a high labour intensive input with little use of machinery. Can grow crops all year round, with usually two or three harvests per year. Little fertiliser is added, therefore leaching limits cultivation to 3 or 4 years. Gathering, fishing and hunting still practised. There is no surplus either for sale or storage. Irregular patches for cultivation. When left alone, this farming system is hard and harsh, but is sustainable.
Concerns	There is deforestation for ranching, mining, lumber, sedentary farming, damming (HEP) and roads. Rivers choked following clearance and deforestation. There is destruction of the native culture and the forced introduction of a 'westernised' lifestyle. There is soil erosion on the fragile land. There is concern over global environmental issues. Land is lost, then fallow periods shorten, putting more pressure on the remaining land. Massive reduction in the number of native people.

HUMAN ENVIRONMENT: RURAL GEOGRAPHY

Questions and Answers

SAQ 4 Study figure 7.2, which shows the relative importance of the elements of shifting cultivation.

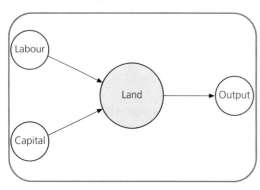

"Shifting cultivation remains an important farming system in many Tropical areas".

For a named location, describe and explain the characteristics of this farming system. *(6 marks)*

Figure 7.2 Elements of shifting cultivation

Answer to SAQ 4

This type of diagram has appeared a few times in the examination. It shows the relationship between labour, land and capital. With shifting cultivation, the emphasis is on the large area of land required. The diagram also shows fairly low levels of capital, output and labour. However the question could be answered without direct reference to the diagram.

Main points Remember to name a location where shifting cultivation is found, e.g. Amazonia, Brazil.

◆ Clearing made in rainforest by 'slash and burn'. Ash left as fertiliser.

◆ Largest trees left in position for protection and to aid regeneration.

◆ Leaching and soil exhaustion takes place quickly, resulting the clearing being abandoned after a few years. Subsistence farming.

◆ Labour intensive with hand planting, weeding and harvesting. Little use of machinery.

◆ Wide range of crops grown. Whole village involved in farming tasks.

◆ Community moves to new clearing, allowing the land to recover (could take 40 years).

◆ If population density low then there is traditionally enough land to allow this land system to be sustainable for many, many years. However this is a real problem today as the land is being squeezed for other more profitable purposes.

Intensive Peasant Farming

Farming System 3

Questions and Answers

SAQ 5 Study Figure 7.3. Annotate it to identify and explain the main features of the landscape and the main farming activities taking place. *(4 marks)*

Figure 7.3 An intensive peasant farming landscape in southern Asia

Answer to SAQ 5

Summary Notes

Location — Monsoon lands of South East Asia, fertile river plains around the Indus and Ganges.

Key words — Subsistence, Sedentary, Cereals, Peasant/traditional, Low technology, Intensive, High output per worker. But change is taking place.

Settlement — The Ganges valley, the 'land of the million villages'. This is a' busy' landscape dominated by villages, terraced and flooded fields and people. Huge numbers of people living densely packed into nuclear villages. Often remote from the big cities. Such densities are only possible due to high fertility of the land and the sustainability of this way of life.

Method — The physical inputs encourage cereals such as rice, wheat, barley and pulses. Two crops per year grown on the fertile alluvium/silt/lava soils. Year round growing season with two harvests. Can be either 'wet' or 'dry' rice cultivated areas. High level of human labour input. Seedlings traditional grown in nurseries and transplanted into fields. Banks (bunds) built up around fields to retain water within flooded fields (padis). Land ploughed by water buffalo and human labour. Never ending battle to maintain the fields. Flooded river plains and terraced hillsides. Fields fertilised by animal manure and drained, leaving rice crop to reach maturity. Traditionally harvested by hand sickle.

Questions and **Answers** continued ➤

HUMAN ENVIRONMENT: RURAL GEOGRAPHY

Questions *and* Answers *continued*

Answer to SAQ 5 continued

Landscape Dominated by the irrigated, padi fields, arranged in strips around the village, often fragmented. Farms are small (90% smaller than 5 hectares), with low levels of mechanisation or use of technology. Terraced hillside. Very little land not cultivated. Visually, this is a landscape of obvious poverty. There is a shortage of food but little actual starvation.

Changes The traditional way of life changing. Mechanisation has increased efficiency, allowing a surplus to be sold in the market. This increases overall levels of wealth. Mechanisation also can increase unemployment, resulting in rural depopulation as many young people migrate to the cities. Fields can be amalgamated, again increasing output. High population increase due to poverty and need for children, falling death rates, and low infant mortality (birth rates now falling). New cash crops have been introduced in some areas, e.g. Kerala, with coconut trees being planted. The caste system is still holding back growth. There is a general feeling that changes tend to favour the already rich, and that the poorer people are improving their quality of life at a slower pace. Green Revolution has brought about changes. Check your notes on the Green Revolution (See more detailed answer below)

SAQ 6 Using data from the table below, describe the changes that have taken place. *(4 marks)*

Agriculture in Ganges Plain, India	1960	1970	1980	1990	2000
% of land irrigated from wells or reservoirs	25	35	60	80	90
Fertiliser applied per hectare (kgms)	20	40	300	400	500
Area sown with High Yield Variety wheat (hectares)	30	1,000	300,000	450,000	600,000
Wheat yield (kgms per hectare)	1,250	1,750	2,500	4,500	6,000

Answer to SAQ 6

This question could be considered straightforward, since it only requires you to describe what you see.

Take each line across in turn and briefly state what you see. Use some of the data, but do not quote endless lines of boring repetition. For example, you could say:

'Fertiliser applied has increased some X25 times from 20kgms per hectare in 1960 to 500kgms per hectare in 2000.'

The Green Revolution is the name given to the use of modern, western style farming techniques in areas such as the Ganges plain, India. Check your notes.

HUMAN ENVIRONMENT: RURAL GEOGRAPHY

Questions and Answers

SAQ 7 Evaluate both the successes and failures associated with the Green Revolution. *(8 marks)*

Answer SAQ 7

An evaluation question asks you to look at both sides of the issue. I would suggest that you describe a number of successes, and then do the same with some of the problems. To evaluate you really should make an attempt to sum it up and say whether the balance of the argument favours the successes or the problems. You should also be able to use your knowledge of a particular area. The lower plains drained by the waters of the River Ganges tend to have experienced both the successes and failures outlined below.

Successes of the Green Revolution	Failures of the Green Revolution
Yields have increased (rice, wheat, maize).	Mechanisation has increased unemployment.
Huge increase in output, possible exports.	HYV seeds require fertilisers and pesticides.
Diet widened out with variety of produce.	Increase in land and water pollution.
Less human suffering through less hunger.	New plant diseases.
More money leading to greater efficiency.	Poor farmers remain poor.
Greater use of irrigation, two crops per year.	Increase in debt due to need to invest.
Demand for fertilisers has created industrial jobs.	Some new crops taste poor.
	Some farmers happy to only grow one crop.
Improved quality of life. Less poverty.	Irrigation is expensive; can lead to salination.
Yields and harvests more reliable.	

What is your conclusion? How do you evaluate the evidence?

That is your decision. It does appear that food output has greatly increased and that there must be less human suffering. However some of this increase will do no more than keep pace with the increase in population. However that is good. Long term, it now seems that population growth is slowing down Future increases in food output will be used by a more stable population. The general level of wealth and health in most of the associated areas has improved. However there is a cost to the environment. It seems also that the poor tend to remain poor, while the rich become richer. What do you think?

HOW TO PASS HIGHER GEOGRAPHY

Questions *and Answers*

SAQ 8   'Intensive peasant farming continues to change and adopt new practices'

For an intensive peasant farming landscape such as in Kerala, India, describe how changes and new practices have affected the people and the farming landscape.   *(6 marks)*

Answer to SAQ 8

The content of your answer has to be clearly located. The marker is now looking for 12 points to get the 6 marks. So what do you have to do? This is really a question about **change**.

You need to describe how the changes have affected the people, **and** also how the changes have affected the landscape. So give some thought to your answer now.

Check your answer with my summary.

◆   More mechanisation has led to fewer animals and fewer people in the fields.

◆   Traditional pattern of small fields and farms being replaced by larger units.

◆   Increased use of chemicals has led to pollution of the land and the water.

◆   More intensive production leads to more irrigation, and a change to the landscape with dams reservoirs and channels.

◆   In the richer areas, there is now a surplus, and the overall quality of living is getting better with improvements in housing, education and health.

Almost forgot about the annotation of Figure 7.3. So here is a very good example from one of my students.

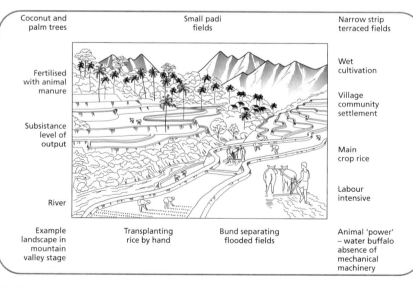

Figure 7.4

Coconut and palm trees — *Small padi fields* — *Narrow strip terraced fields* — *Fertilised with animal manure* — *Wet cultivation* — *Subsistance level of output* — *Village community settlement* — *Main crop rice* — *River* — *Labour intensive* — *Example landscape in mountain valley stage* — *Transplanting rice by hand* — *Bund separating flooded fields* — *Animal 'power' – water buffalo absence of mechanical machinery*

Well done! Another Environment unit completed. Remember the key words: systems, landscape and change.

Chapter 8

HUMAN ENVIRONMENT: INDUSTRIAL GEOGRAPHY

What You Should Know

- Industrial Systems
- Industrial Landscapes
- Industrial Change

Industrial Systems

Questions and Answers

SAQ 1 Industrial activity can be classified into 4 main categories. Match the *heading* with the *tail*.

Heading	Tail	
1 Primary	A	A new category (subdivision of tertiary) involving research, development, information or consultancy
2 Secondary (manufacturing)	B	When raw materials are made into finished products such as cars or televisions
3 Tertiary (service)	C	When raw materials are extracted as in fishing, farming or mining
4 Quaternary	D	When a service is offered as in shops, offices or in health care

Answer to SAQ 1

1=C, 2=B, 3=D, 4=A

Hints and Tips

Time to check through your notes. Possibly time again to remind you of the best way to revise. You really need to have a degree in organisation skills. Try to keep all your notes for each theme together. Teachers do love giving out handout sheets. The trouble is you probably decided that you would read through these 'pearls of wisdom' later. Bad idea!

Hints and *Tips* continued ➤

Hints and Tips continued

Read the notes and make sure that they are properly labelled. Invest in ring binders. You know when friends ask you what you want for Christmas – well, forget about the CDs, money and clothes. Ask for index cards, binders and highlighter pens!

It is best to go for active revision. Read for ten minutes, sit back and think about what you have read, then jot down some thoughts. It is also a really good idea to have a note of what the SQA expect you to know. Keep your homework exercises and of course keep this book handy.

It appears that in the past the UK had a high proportion of its workers in primary industry with very few in the manufacturing or service areas. As the country developed, there was growth in the secondary sector, with a more modest growth in the tertiary. This trend continued with further development until the service sector became the major employing group.

Questions and Answers

SAQ 2 Describe the trends shown on the table below. Explain how these trends could have a social impact within an area. *(4 marks)*

UK Employment Structure 1950 to 2000 (%)						
	1950	1960	1970	1980	1990	2000
Primary	7	6	5	5	4	4
Secondary	60	59	56	52	48	39
Tertiary	30	31	32	33	34	37
Quaternary	3	4	7	10	14	20

Note that in some questions and tables, the figures for tertiary and quaternary are added together

Answer to SAQ 2

Note that there is a moving pattern over the years; therefore there is a change in overall employment structure. Note the decline in the primary and secondary sectors. The reduction in secondary sector is very significant. There is a steady growth in the tertiary sector, but there is massive growth within the quaternary sector. Impact would be felt in those areas of the UK that traditionally had a base in the secondary or manufacturing sector. Old industrial areas such as Glasgow or Manchester would be most affected by closures and redundancies. In such employment 'black-spots' the problem is not just the decline of the old heavy industries (after all change is to be expected and even encouraged)

Questions and Answers continued ➤

Questions and Answers continued

Answer to SAQ 2 continued

but the failure to attract the new growth industries and jobs. With continuing decline in the primary sector, those in farming areas would need to seek alternative jobs in the growing tertiary and quaternary sectors.

SAQ 3 Describe the similarities and differences in employment patterns as shown in the table below.

If Portugal continues to develop, how would you expect the employment pattern to change over the next 25 years? *(5 marks)*

Country	% employed in each category 2003			
	Primary	Secondary	Tertiary	Quaternary
UK	4	39	37	20
Germany	7	42	34	17
France	13	39	35	13
Portugal	27	33	33	7

Answer to SAQ 3

You could note the similar balance across the countries, with % in primary industry always lowest and % in tertiary/quaternary the highest. For statistical purposes, often the tertiary and the quaternary are added together. Contrast between extremes could be highlighted, e.g. the 4% in UK primary to be contrasted with 27% in Portugal. Note general similarity in totals down the table for secondary and for tertiary.

The trend expected would be that the primary figure would decline, e.g. in farming as people leave the land to get more money and security of employment in the secondary and tertiary sectors. Secondary industry would continue to increase in importance, as would employment in the growing tertiary and quaternary sectors.

Questions and Answers

All categories of industry can be measured against an **Industrial System Model of 'inputs, processes and outputs**.'

Figure 8.1 Inputs, processes and outputs

SAQ 4   Select an example from each of the 4 categories, e.g. a dairy farmer, a crisp manufacturer, a dentist and a computer consultant, and apply the job to this model and see if it works.

I have not provided an answer to all four categories; however I have suggested a structure for 'pickled onion crisp manufacture'.

Answer SAQ 4

Inputs	Processes	Outputs
Potatoes	Assembly	Crisps
Onions/vinegar/salt	Packaging	
Land/labour/power	Design of bag	
Investment money		
All the other 'E' number ingredients!		

Industrial Location

It is not by chance that industries establish and develop in an area. You need to be able to apply those location factors either to an individual industry or to an area such as Central Scotland, South Wales or the Ruhr in Germany. You can choose the area within Europe. Another point worth thinking about is that those factors have changed over the years. In the 19th century the physical factors were more important, while throughout the 20th and into the 21st centuries human and economic factors became more important.

Selecting the location for a new industry or business is important. If you get it wrong the company will go bust! If your costs are greater than your competitors, then the buyers of your product or service will usually go to the cheaper/ best 'value for money' option.

Questions and Answers

SAQ 5 Check through your notes on 'location factors', study Figure 8.2 and take some notes to show that you understand each of the factors.

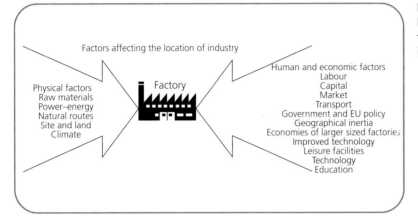

Factors affecting the location of industry

Physical factors
Raw materials
Power–energy
Natural routes
Site and land
Climate

Factory

Human and economic factors
Labour
Capital
Market
Transport
Government and EU policy
Geographical inertia
Economies of larger sized factories
Improved technology
Leisure facilities
Technology
Education

Figure 8.2
Factors affecting the location of industry

SAQ 6 With reference to a named industrial concentration in the European Union:

(a) Explain why physical factors have led to the growth of early industry, and

(b) Suggest why human and economic factors have become more important in accounting for the location of industry today. *(9 marks)*

Answer to SAQ 6

Credit throughout will be acknowledged for specific references to industries and their locations within the selected area. It is vital that your answer is based on a named example, e.g. South Wales or Central Scotland.

Any relevant reference to authentic physical factors such as:

◆ Proximity to raw materials such as charcoal, coal, iron ore and limestone, e.g. in the rise of iron working in South Wales. Such resources were often easy to exploit.

◆ Water power giving way to steam power, provided by coal, e.g. textile industry in the North of England.

◆ Valley floors in South Wales for example, were flat and easy for building on.

◆ The importance of water transport, e.g. canals and barges.

Any relevant reference to authentic human and economic factors such as:

◆ The need to be close to motorway links or air links for ease of movement of materials and finished goods.

◆ The part played by the government and EU incentives in attracting new industries to depressed areas.

Questions and *Answers* continued ➤

HUMAN ENVIRONMENT: INDUSTRIAL GEOGRAPHY

Questions and Answers continued

Answer to SAQ 6 continued

◆ The importance of being near a large market for the product to be sold.

◆ The significance of a well-trained and motivated workforce.

◆ The concept of 'geographical inertia' being responsible for the continued existence of some industries in a particular area.

◆ In order to remain competitive and avoid import restrictions, foreign-owned companies choose to have a base in the UK.

◆ The opportunities provided for high-tech businesses locating close to universities.

Map work and Industry

We cannot predict the map. There are 4 environment questions where an OS map could be included. If the map is of a rural environment, then the questions are more than likely to be linked to the Hydrosphere or the Lithosphere. If the map is urban focused, then the questions will be found in the Industry and Urban Cores.

Map questions take time and it is easy to spend too much time on one. Practise tends to make you more efficient. To make sure that you focus on the correct area of the map, I strongly advise you to use a highlighter pen on the bits you have been asked to study. So let's have a go at a question.

Questions and Answers

SAQ 7   Adapted from the 2003 examination

Study the map extract (Ellesmere Port), Figure 8.3 and the location map Figure 8.4.

With reference to at least 2 industrial areas (select from areas A, B and C) describe and explain the evidence that suggests the area is attractive for the location of industry.   *(5 marks)*

Questions and *Answers* continued ➤

Questions and Answers continued

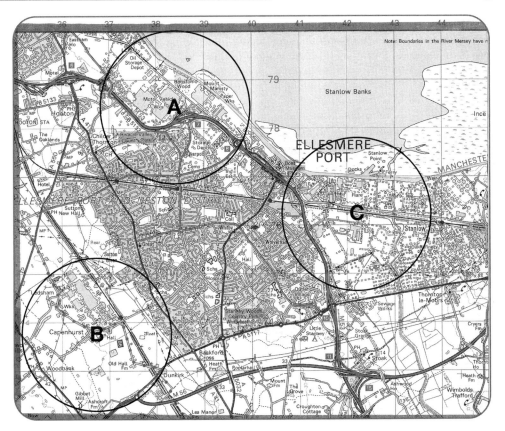

Figure 8.3 OS map extract Ellesmere Port

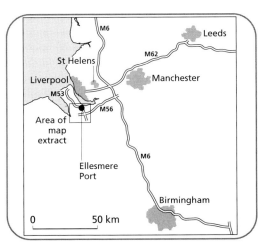

Figure 8.4 Location map of Ellesmere Port

Answer to SAQ 7

What is it you are asked to do?

You have to identify location factors from the map. You must use grid references, and give examples from a number of industrial areas.

The instructions given to markers said that for full marks you must refer to at least two areas, and that the marker can award up to 2 marks for correct and appropriate grid references.

Questions and *Answers* continued ➢

Questions and Answers continued

- Access to A class roads (A5117) or motorway (M53) for transportation of raw material inputs or final products (relevant to areas A, B. C) Give grid ref.
- Good access to cities such as Manchester or Liverpool by motorway, useful for market (areas A, B, C).
- Note the presence of the Manchester Ship Canal, used for transporting raw materials and finished products.
- Excellent rail network within extract (Areas A, B, C). Give grid ref.
- Canal and a tidal river for the import of heavy raw materials (Areas A, C) Give grid ref.
- Plenty of room for expansion (Areas A, B). Give grid ref.
- Flat land suitable for easy construction (Areas A, B, C).
- Nearby settlements for workforce, e.g. Ellesmere Port for all three areas.

Industrial Landscapes

Industrial landscapes have changed greatly over the years. Study Figures 8.5 and 8.6.

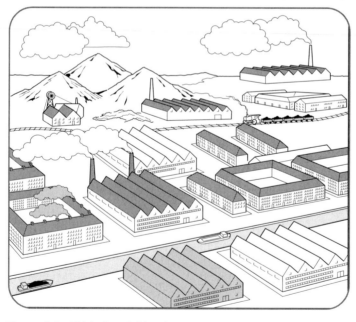

Figure 8.5 Old industrial landscape

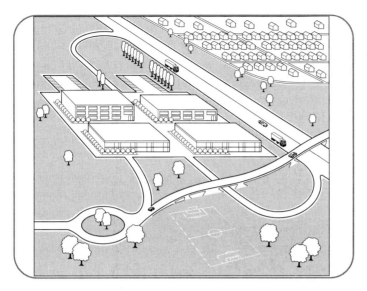

Figure 8.6 New industrial landscape

Summary

A summary of the main features

Old industrial landscape

Close to water/weirs (power).

Close to housing and city centre (grid-iron street pattern).

Crowded environment with little open space.

Rely on canal/railway transport links.

Derelict land/wasteland, old rundown buildings. Industry in decline.

Large (brick/stone) buildings; tall brick chimney stacks.

Poor road links/congested roads/narrow streets.

Lack of space for expansion or redevelopment associated with heavy industry (iron and steel, machinery, mills).

'Brown earth sites'.

Close to coal fields.

Polluted rivers.

Air, land, visual and noise pollution.

Low amenity surroundings.

Low-cost terraced and tenement housing.

Water used as a raw material.

New industrial landscape

'Green field sites'

Clean, attractive environment on rural-urban fringe

Separate modern housing adjacent, but not on same site.

Theme site sharing, e.g. Science Park.

70% of land is open space.

High amenity surroundings.

High quality environment for working.

Access by road and by air.

Often linked to colleges and universities.

Landscape planned and organised.

Electricity powered.

Often 'light' industry based on electronics, food technology.

Cheaper land.

Room for development and expansion.

Often in 'parks' to exchange information with similar firms.

Industries associated with growth.

Questions and Answers

SAQ 8 Annotate Figures 8.5 and 8.6 using the most appropriate features from the above list.

You could be asked to describe landscapes from an OS map. Tick those features above which could reasonably be recognised from a map.

I think that you can self correct this task.

SAQ 9 Study OS map Cardiff, Figure 8.7 and Figure 8.8, location of contrasting industrial areas.

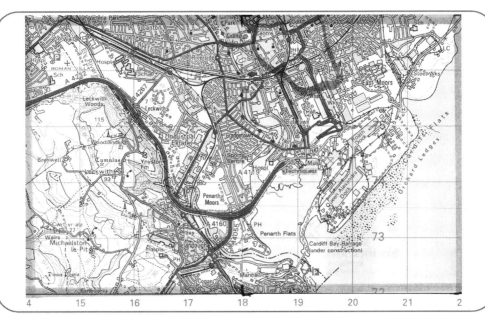

Figure 8.7 OS map extract Cardiff

a) Describe and explain the physical and human factors which encouraged industry to locate in areas A and B. *(6 marks)*

b) Areas A and B seem to offer contrasting industrial landscapes, one being old and the other one newer. Match up the age of landscape with the two areas and, using map evidence, describe the differences in the two landscapes. *(6 marks)*

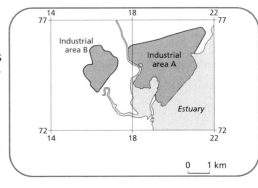

Figure 8.8 Industrial areas Cardiff

Questions and *Answers continued* ➤

Questions and Answers continued

Answer to SAQ 9

a) In some ways this is similar to SAQ 6. Here you have been asked to separate your answer into physical and human factors. What's the difference? Once again, you get marks for giving appropriate grid references. Answers could include the following,

Area A   Physical factors

◆ Plenty of flat land for building large factories, such as the steelworks in 2175.

◆ Plenty of land for growth and storage, such as around Roath Dock (2074).

◆ Water source for cooling, processing and transport.

◆ Mudflats which could be reclaimed.

◆ Close to deep water for transport or raw materials and for delivery to the market.

Area B   Physical factors

◆ Flat land for new buildings, growth and storage, such as Penarth Moor (1773).

◆ Fairly close to deep water for transport or raw materials and for delivery to the market.

Area A   Human factors

◆ Good communications. Railway sidings (1974), good roads close to the docks (A4232), even a heliport (2075), bus and railway station (1875).

◆ Enclosed docks and warehouses.

◆ Nearby labour force. Note the grid pattern within Grangetown (1774).

◆ Not shown on map but area does qualify for Government and European Union money.

◆ Some attractive looking countryside to the west of the study zone.

Area B   Human factors

◆ Good communications. Railway line and station (1774), good roads (A4232).

◆ Enclosed docks and warehouses nearby.

◆ Nearby labour force. Note Grangetown (1774) as well as the settlement to the south (1772).

◆ Not shown on map but area does qualify for government and European Union money.

◆ Some attractive-looking countryside to the west of the study zone.

b) Industrial area A is an old landscape. What is the evidence? The area contains dockside industries, warehouses, railway tracks, docks and quays. The area also contains several references to 'works' (e.g. 196754) as well as a steel works (215759). Check back to my list of old industry features. You can tick off what you see on the map.

Industrial area B is a newer industrial estate and landscape. What is the evidence? Once again check back to the list of new industry features and tick them off.

HOW TO PASS HIGHER GEOGRAPHY

Industrial Change

Of course nothing remains the same forever. With improvements in design, changing technology and personal preferences, industry has had to adapt and change to meet new demands and trends. Failure to innovate will simply cause factories to go bust.

Check your notes on industrial growth, industrial decline, impact of industrial change and options for the future. Once again you must have detailed knowledge about one area either in the UK or in the EU.

What were the main reasons for industrial change? We will start by looking at industrial decline. You must realise that we usually think of change equalling industrial decline. This is not always the case, and change can also be a positive feature allowing new opportunities to be developed. Depending on your case study area, you may have recognised the following as factors resulting in decline.

◆ Local supplies of a raw material running out (for example coal seams in South Wales).

◆ Local raw materials becoming too expensive in the face of cheaper imports.

◆ Industries failing to respond to new techniques, or to new markets or products or simply not understanding that change is a natural factor, and that you must innovate or go out of business.

◆ The growth of overseas competition based on lower-cost labour, better techniques and more modern equipment, resulting in a cheaper and/ or a superior product (for example, digital and electronic equipment made in Korea rather than the UK).

◆ Loss of old established markets.

◆ The need to have a site on the coast, or on flat land for development.

◆ Fluctuating world demand and changing patterns.

◆ Trends towards globalisation at the expense of individual countries (for example the Dyson company switching production of their floor cleaners from the UK to the Far East).

The story of industrial change in the UK is not just about decline. It is also about new industrial development and opportunity. Possibly not as much as we would have liked, but if you study the present industrial geography of areas in, for example, the New Towns of Scotland, there are many positive signs of development.

Impact of Change

Negative Features

Unemployment increasing.

Older men hit hard by unemployment.

Derelict environment.

Unattractive to new industrial opportunities.

Financial impact with families hit hard.

Reduction in purchasing power.

Local Authorities lose rates/rent.

Spin-off closures in the community: shops/garages/transport.

Loss of community spirit especially in areas such as mining/heavy industry

Social impact within the home, e.g. divorce/alcoholism/suicide.

Opportunities and Positive Features

Polluted rivers, land, air Creation of a 'ghost' town.

Out-migration of the young and dynamic.

New growth industries, e.g. in electronics, communications.

New jobs, new skills, new opportunities (but often for low skills with more opportunities

for women).

A 'multiplier' effect with 'spin-off' jobs.

Financial boost for local authority.

Family income increases with positive impact in local shops, travel agents, car showrooms, etc.

General growth in housing and transport.

Easy to attract new investment into a growth area.

What you should now do is consider the impact of change in your selected case study example, and select those issues relevant to that area.

HUMAN ENVIRONMENT: INDUSTRIAL GEOGRAPHY

Questions and Answers

SAQ 9 Study Figure 8.9, which shows a map of the NE of England and traditional industries.

The industries shown here have all declined since 1980.

For NE England **or any other** industrial concentrations in the European Union that you have studied

a) Describe the factors responsible for the early growth and development of the area. *(4 marks)*

b) Explain why older traditional industries have declined over the last 25 years. *(5 marks)*

c) For your chosen industrial concentration describe the social and environmental consequences which have accompanied this industrial decline. *(5 marks)*

Questions and *Answers* continued ➤

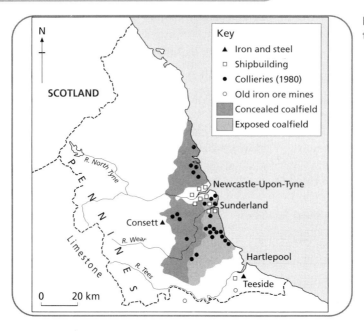

Figure 8.9 NE England traditional industries

Answer to SAQ 9

You really have the background information to answer this question. However let us look at what you have to do. Note that while the map shows data for the NE of England, the question clearly asks you to consider any area that you know. An 'industrial concentration' should be of a reasonable geographical area. For example you could use South Wales, or the Ruhr in Germany or the Industrial Central Belt of Scotland as examples. Avoid small areas since it id difficult to get full marks from a limited example. I once had a student who used an industrial estate outside Kilmarnock!

NE England

a) There were plentiful supplies of coking coal along the coast and inland, as well as blackband iron ore from the Cleveland Hills south of the River Tees around Teeside. Limestone could easily be brought down from the Pennines. These three raw materials formed the basics for the early iron and steel industry. The estuaries of the Tyne, Tees and Wear encouraged the development of ports and trade links were established across the North Sea to Europe. Shipbuilding grew in importance.

b) Decline was linked to the closures of all the iron ore mines and many of the coalfields. Cheaper raw materials were imported. The traditional industries such as iron and steel and shipbuilding collapsed following foreign competition, the loss of markets, world economic swings, poor sites, expensive labour costs and a failure to modernise.

Have a look at an answer for the second part of SAQ 9, written by a student.

Questions and Answers continued ➤

Questions and Answers continued

'My area is going to be the industrial wasteland along the River Clyde from Glasgow to Greenock. **(½)** Since 1980 this area has declined both in terms of the number of jobs and the number of companies. **(½)** Shipbuilding **(½)** has almost disappeared and nearly all other industries have gone.

Ships can now be built cheaper **(½)** in other countries (e.g. Spain or Korea) **(½)**. And we have lost our market. **(½)** The local supplies of coal and iron ore **(½)** have gone and expensive raw material would have to be bought in. **(½)** The River Clyde became too narrow for the big ships to be built and launched. **(½)** During the 1980s the workers and the managers did not get on, and costly strikes **(½)** gave the Clyde a bad reputation worldwide, **(½)** and the ships seemed to not be so well built **(½)** or delivered on time. **(½)** There was a depression in the UK during the 1980s **(½)** and we did not seem to order as many ships. The result was that yards closed (such as 'Fairfields or John Brown) **(½)** and the riverside fell into a state of decay.'

So how would this score? Credit is given for an appropriate case study. This one easily gets full marks. Now mark your own answer.

The last part of this question takes in the content from the 'Impact' summary above. However, can I remind you that you do need to clearly refer to an area, and make several named connections to that area? It is not good enough to simply name a region and then never refer to it again.

c) Of course a government is expected to step in and provide additional support for a depressed area. Change can affect an area, and the problems created are hardly the fault of the local people. They cannot be ignored, and may require a little additional assistance and support from the local authority, the Scottish Executive, the national government, or even support form the European Union. So what can be done?

◆ Create a site with a period of free or low rates.

◆ Provide grants for machinery and equipment.

◆ Establish training schemes for the workers and job creation grants.

◆ Create improved access to the market by improving roads.

◆ Assist with improvements to the infrastructure, e.g. water and power.

◆ Set up enterprise boards and inward investment specialists.

◆ Encourage new overseas investment.

◆ Create a willing, educated workforce.

◆ Create new opportunities
e.g. old coal mines into industrial museums or an old iron works into a heritage centre.

Apply these points to your case study.

HUMAN ENVIRONMENT: URBAN

If you have been working through this revision book in the order of the questions in the examination, then this is the eighth and final environment unit. So almost there! This environment unit is usually linked with the interactions application unit, 'Urban Change and its Management'. There is overlap.

What You Should Know

The main idea is that settlements provide a range of employment, services, and residential opportunities, which may be located in different parts of the settlement. You need to have detailed knowledge of one large urban concentration from an Economically More Developed Country. (EMDC) The key words are **systems**, **zones** and **change**. You need to have knowledge and understanding of:

◆ Urban systems

◆ Urban zones

◆ Urban change (post 1950)

Hints and Tips

Your teacher will probably have given you past questions. It is important that you know what has been asked before. A problem worth mentioning is that since this question is traditionally number 8 in the paper, a small number of pupils have run out of time and the answer may be rushed. There is a high chance that urban questions will be linked to an OS map. That's good since you have to mix the theory with the practical and you have the answer visible on the map. All you have to do is read the map.

As you can see from the SQA syllabus above, you need to have a detailed case study. Many schools study Edinburgh or London or Manchester. To illustrate the theory, Glasgow is the city used in this book.

Questions and Answers

SAQ 1 Check back to your notes and give a definition for the following keywords: Settlement, Site and Situation, Rural, Urban, Urbanisation, Conurbation, Suburbanisation, Counter-urbanisation, Urban sprawl.

Answer to SAQ 1

As you work through this unit, the answers can be checked.

Site and Situation

Site is the exact location of a settlement, the actual land on which it is built. To explain site, it is necessary to look at physical and economic/human reasons. The physical factors were probably more important in the past.

- **Relief**   High enough to be safe from flooding, yet low enough to be sheltered from the wind.
- **Defence**   Sites such as on a hilltop, above a steep slope or on the inside of a meander, were desirable.
- **Transport**   At a crossroads, a bridging point over a river, or at the 'head' of a valley.
- **Soil**   A deep fertile soil, on gently sloping land made farming possible.
- **Water supply** For drinking, irrigation, cooking and cleaning.
- **Resources**   Such as building stone, coal or timber (for building, fuel for cooking and warmth).

Situation is the location of a settlement in relation to the surrounding area, e.g. fertile soil, valleys, hills, coast, river, and routes. The site and situation factors listed above can encourage the growth of a settlement.

Case Study Site and situation and the growth of Glasgow

Questions and Answers

SAQ 2   Match column A with column B.

Glasgow was once just another small village positioned beside the river Clyde. However it grew at a rate that soon left all the other villages behind. A combination of physical factors and chance made Glasgow grow from the early 13th century.

Column A	Column B
A The river Clyde	1 provided a good site for a fort, which gave protection to local people
B The early bridge	2 such as coal, iron ore and limestone encouraged manufacturing industry
C A ridge of higher ground	3 also encouraged the growth of a church (later a cathedral) and a University
D The raised site provided	4 converged on Glasgow and reinforced the city as a communication centre
E The fertile soil allowed	5 encouraged routes to converge at this point, and cross the river

Questions and *Answers* continued ➤

Questions and Answers continued

Column A	Column B
F The secure site	6 was shallow enough to be crossed by people
G The river was deepened	7 a dry point site above the level of the flood waters
H The west coast location	8 opened opportunities for tobacco, sugar and cotton manufacturing in the city
I The Atlantic trade	9 allowing the largest ships of the day to reach into the heart of the city
J Crucial raw materials	10 the city became a service centre with a strong 'pull' across central Scotland
K Railways and roads	11 a food surplus to be produced and a thriving market established for trading
L As the population grew	12 placed Glasgow in a perfect position for trade across the Atlantic to America

Answer to SAQ 2

A=6, B=5, C=1, D=7, E=11, F=3, G=9, H=12, I=8, J=2, K=4, L=10

SAQ 3 For any city you have studied in the economically more developed world, show how its original site and situation encouraged its growth. *(4 marks)*

Answer to SAQ 3

Check out the notes above for Glasgow. Do you have another case study? Check it out now.

Settlement Hierarchy

Settlements can be arranged in rank order, a hierarchy, using criteria such as population size or number and range of services found.

Sphere of Influence (SOI)

The SOI is the area served by a settlement (also known as the catchment area). The importance of a settlement is linked to its size, which in turn is linked to the range and number of services found and its SOI. 'The larger the settlement the greater the number of services, the greater the SOI.' SOI is linked to the 'range', the maximum distance people are prepared to travel to use a service, and the 'threshold', the minimum number of people needed to support a service.

HUMAN ENVIRONMENT: URBAN

Service order	Range	Threshold	Examples
Low order	Small and limited area. 'Local'.	Can be as low as a few hundred people.	Convenience shops selling newspapers, milk, bread. The local 'Spar'.
Middle order	Within a town and surrounding villages.	A few thousand people.	The sort of shops you get in a town but not a village, such as a shoe shop, card shop.
High order	Large. People will travel a distance into the centre.	Large number of people needed. Transport links important.	City centre services and specialised shops. Comparison shops. Department stores.

In a village such as Dundonald, Ayrshire, with a population of 3,000, there are half a dozen shops/ services (chemist, newsagent, butcher, 'takeaway', general convenience store). Locals buy their day-to-day basics. However for the weekly food shop, or for clothes, or for services such as a travel agent or a 'Chicken Kiev' from Marks and Spencers, the people travel to Kilmarnock or Ayr. For that 'special' outfit, or more specialised services (jewellers) or for 'comparison' shopping, they will travel to Glasgow.

Function of a settlement

The function of a settlement is what it does. All settlements have shared functions, such as residential or housing. Other settlements may be notable for certain functions such as administration (government) recreation and tourism, industrial, commercial (shops/offices), services (public buildings/ schools/hospitals) and transport.

Questions and Answers

SAQ 4 What function do you associate with: Blackpool, London, Oxford, Canterbury, Manchester, Dover, Newcastle?

Answer to SAQ 4

Please note that your answers may differ but could equally be correct

Blackpool	Tourism, recreation and conferences	Manchester	Industrial, leisure
London	Administration, shopping, transport	Dover	Ferry port and terminal
Oxford	University and education	Newcastle	Industry, port, shopping
Canterbury	Cathedral and religion		

HOW TO PASS HIGHER GEOGRAPHY

Urban Zones

What You Should Know

Geographers try to look for order and patterns. Think of a large town or city near you. You should be able to recognise different zones or areas.

In Higher Geography we recognise the following distinct areas.

Central Business District (CBD)

19th-century housing (old) **and** 19th-century industry (old), both part of what is often referred to as the 'inner city'.

20th-century housing (new and sometimes referred to as 'suburbia') **and** 20th Century industry (new).

You should be able to name and describe the key features of each of the five zones. A common examination question is linked to an OS map and asks you to recognise these zones (with reasons). Another question is sometimes linked to land use transects. (See **SAQ 6**.) Again, you will be asked to describe and explain the differences in land use across a city. You should have detailed knowledge of one named city.

Questions and Answers

SAQ 5   Take each of the five key land use zones associated with an urban area, and make a summary of the main features you would expect to find.

Answer to SAQ 5

Central Business District

CBD Near the geographical centre. Concentration of roads. Gridiron pattern. Maximum access to public transport. Look for bus and train stations. High density of buildings concerned with retail, commerce and finance, legal, entertainment (cinemas/clubs/theatres). Public buildings, (town hall, museums, churches), tourist office, universities, concert halls. Little open space, industry or housing. Pedestrianisation of streets. High density of vehicles and pedestrians. Wide range of comparison and specialist shops. Modern shopping malls. Buildings often multi-storied. See notes on changes and problems.

19th-century housing (old)

Part of what is called the inner city, surrounding the CBD. Grew rapidly during industrialisation over a 100 years ago. A mixture of high-density tenement or terraced housing, often in a rectangular, 'grid-iron' pattern. Houses constructed quickly and cheaply. Slum housing. Busy roads pass through the housing areas. Lacking open space,

Questions and *Answers* continued ➤

Questions and **Answers** continued

Answer to SAQ 5 continued

and usually linked with old 19th century industry. Scene of very extensive change and redevelopment. See notes on changes and problems.

19th-century industry (old)

Part of what is called the inner city, surrounding the CBD. Grew rapidly during industrialisation over a 100 years ago. Close to housing (source of labour) and linked to railways, canals and rivers. Buildings large, cluttered, dense network of narrow streets and the environment is usually marked by dereliction and decay. See notes on changes and problems.

20th-century housing (new)

Local authority and private housing in separate estates. Style and density does change the closer you get to the edge of the settlement. Also known as the suburbs/outskirts. Density lower with semi- detached and detached houses, as well as slightly more densely packed flats and rows of houses. Street patterns often smooth and curved, (crescents) with cul-de-sacs. Far more open space. Busy roads avoid going through housing zone.

20th-century industry (new)

Usually separate from housing, on sites with room for growth and expansion. Linked more to roads and motorways. The environment will be landscaped, less polluted and accessible for the labour force. Look out for separate industrial estates, with many factories in one complex. A more recent development is the out of town centre business parks and even shopping complexes.

SAQ 6 Study Figure 9.1, which shows changes in land use from the CBD to the edge of a typical city. With reference to a city you have studied in the economically more developed world, (EMD), describe and explain the differences in land use from the centre to the edge. *(8 marks)*

OR **describe and explain the differences in land use from two selected zones.** *(6 marks)*

Answer to SAQ 6

Note that you are asked to describe **and** explain.

There are two ways in which you can answer this question. You could take each zone in turn and briefly describe land use. Or you could take particular land uses, e.g. shops or housing, and note the differences as you move outwards. The answer below came from one of my students.

'In Glasgow, land use in the CBD is dominated by two activities, namely shops and offices along for example, Argyll and Sauchiehall Street (over 85% of land use). The missing 15%,

Questions *and Answers* continued

Answer to SAQ 6 continued

public buildings (George Square) and a little industry. There is little open space or housing. This is because the CBD is the focus for cars, buses and trains. People want to travel into the city to shop and work. For the same reason land is very expensive in the centre and only offices and shops can afford the high rent. In the outer zone (c), housing is the main use (60%), for example in Bearsden, with plenty of open space (20%), such as parks and golf courses (Williamwood). There is some industry and shops for local people to buy their goods (e.g. Newton Mearns). This is because there is less competition for land and land prices are far lower.'

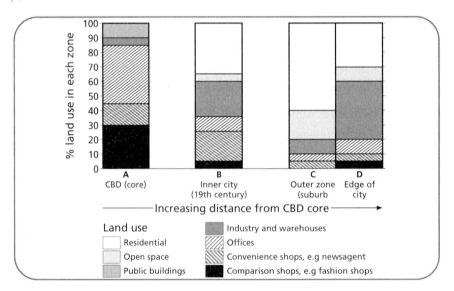

Figure 9.1 Land use transect from the CBD to the edge of the city

An explanation of land use zones in a city

There are three factors that can explain the sequence of zones: i.e. accessibility, age of development and land values. Cities are also known as 'central places'.

Accessibility. The CBD is the focus of roads and rail routes. It is the most accessible part of a city. For that reason, most shops and offices are located in the centre.

Age of development. In the 19th century the main growth and demand was for housing and industry. This explains the position of the inner city zone. During the latter part of the 20th century, the demand was for housing, separate industry and an attractive environment. This explains the sequencing at the edge of the city. See the Interaction Unit on urban change and its management for more detail.

Land Values. There is competition for land in the most accessible part of the city, space is limited and due to this, land prices are high. As competition decreases land values fall as distance from the CBD increases. This is called 'distance decay'.

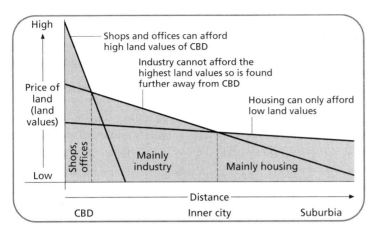

Figure 9.2 Distance decay model

How does this affect land use?

Let's consider shops and offices, industry and residential land uses. Shops and offices need to locate in the CBD to be accessible. This explains the number of high-rise buildings making use of the limited ground space. Think of the commercial premises you would find in the CBD. Only those making large profits can afford the costs, especially the high rents due to the high value of the land. Other users of space (e.g. for industry/residential) will avoid such expensive areas.

Early industrial development tagged around the CBD at what was then the edge of the settlement. Railways and canals linked onto this area. Since people walked to their work, houses developed alongside the industry. In time this mixed housing/industry zone was engulfed with more housing developments, and the site became congested and unsuitable for modern industries, which required more space and access to road communications. New industries sought edge of city sites, with space and lower land value costs.

Generally as you move outwards land values are lower. This explains the lower densities of housing, the open spaces with parks and golf courses and ideal sites for relocated offices, industrial estates and 'out of town shopping' developments.

For residential purposes the newer developments nearer the outer part of the city/towns are more desirable. Houses have space for gardens, expansion and the planned environment gives a better quality of life.

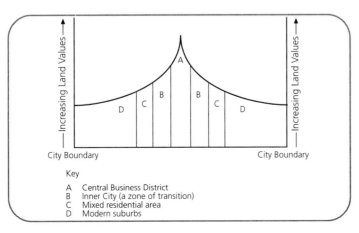

Key

A Central Business District
B Inner City (a zone of transition)
C Mixed residential area
D Modern suburbs

Study Figure 9.3, which shows a model of land values and land use zones across a city.

Figure 9.3

Questions and Answers

SAQ 7   With reference to Figure 9.3 and a named city in the EMD world, **describe and account** for the likely land uses to be observed in any two of the zones A, B, C or D.   *(6 marks)*

Answer to SAQ 7

Note that you must refer to a named city. The notes above have actually covered the content for this answer. If I had to sit the Geography exam again, I would pick zones A and B, making sure I named the characteristic features and give reasons linked to accessibility, age of development and land values.

Urban landscapes and OS maps

Checking back with the syllabus, and through a review of questions over the last 10 years, it would seem that you could get questions that will ask you to:

Suggest the likely function of selected zones and be able to give reasons

Describe the contrasts in residential/urban environments and be able to give reasons

Comment on the likely quality of an environment

Use map evidence to show that the city has a particular function, e.g. tourist resort

Comment on original sites/contrast sites and describe subsequent growth

Select one or more zones on a map and suggest the changes that may have taken place in recent years

When you are to asked to comment on, or contrast residential or urban **environments**, you can mention the following:

Example

♦ The density of built-up areas (e.g. high density/low density).

♦ Whether there are open spaces.

♦ Street patterns (e.g. grid-iron/crescents).

♦ Buildings (e.g. churches/hospitals/schools).

♦ Possible age of housing and style (e.g. detached/tenements).

♦ Transport patterns (e.g. high-density main roads/quiet local).

♦ Recreational land (e.g. parks/ golf courses/woodland).

♦ Possible gardens (front/and or rear).

♦ Proximity of industry/pollution potential.

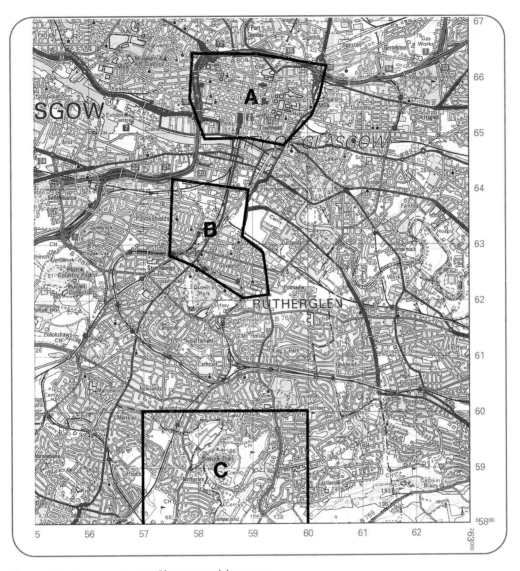

Figure 9.4 A map extract, Glasgow, with zones

Questions and Answers

SAQ 8   Study zone A on the map of Glasgow.

a)   Suggest the likely functions of zone A. Back up your answer with map evidence.   *(3 marks)*

b)   Study zones B and C. Which zone is likely to be the oldest?

For both zones B and C, and using evidence from the map, describe and contrast the environments you would expect to find.   *(6 marks)*

Questions and *Answers* continued ➤

Questions and Answers continued

Answer to SAQ 8

a) Zone A is clearly the CBD. You can use 4-figure or exact 6-figure grid references. Even with my failing eyesight I can nevertheless make out many of the characteristic features that were listed in my answer for SAQ 5. Although routes do converge on the CBD, you can also make out the more recent ring road around the centre. You can see a bus station, the main railway station, the town hall, many churches, colleges, a university, a museum and the information centre for tourists. The buildings are densely packed, with little open space. The street pattern is gridiron.

b) Zone B is older. This seems to be a 19th century urban residential/ industrial environment. The streets are built up, with little open space and with a gridiron street pattern. There is evidence of industry, with a dense network of roads, a railway line and station and an industrial railway track. Apart from some churches, there is little evidence of other service or public buildings. There is little evidence of open space and recreation ground. This zone would probably be crowded, congested and polluted.

c) Zone C is more modern. The housing density is far lower, and the houses are likely to be detached/semi-detached. The street patterns are more associated with post-1960. Note the curvilinear pattern with crescents and cul-de-sacs. There is open space, with woodland, parks, golf courses and a nature trail. The roads will be quiet and the overall environment would probably be judged to be more relaxed, less polluted and attractive than zone B.

Land Use Models

We have recognised different zones within urban areas. Geographers have attempted to show such patterns in diagram form. The purpose of such models is to simplify urban structures and help us to understand how cities grow. There are three main models that appear in all the books. The concentric model (Burgess) is the simplest, which notes that cities develop in 'rings' from a central source (the CBD). It is based on age of building and wealth. The city is older at its core and newer at the fringes, and assumes that growth is even in all directions. It ignores physical features (rivers/hills/coasts) and ignores the influence of routes (railways/canals/roads/rivers). It does not really consider the variety of fringe land uses in the modern city (such as industrial estates/green belts). See Figure 9.5. The sector model (Hoyt) introduces the idea of sectors/wedges within the concentric rings, linked to roads/railways/canals/rivers. Industry would be attracted to such areas and low quality housing would follow. See Figure 9.6. American geographers devised both models. A British model has been suggested that seems to work well when applied to an industrial city. It combines the idea of outward growth, sector growth lined to industry, combined with large-scale redevelopment and urban sprawl. See Figure 9.7. All the features found within each of the rings and sectors have been discussed elsewhere in this unit.

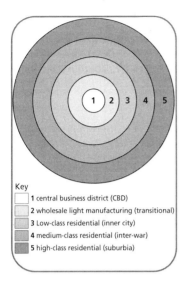

Key
1 central business district (CBD)
2 wholesale light manufacturing (transitional)
3 Low-class residential (inner city)
4 medium-class residential (inter-war)
5 high-class residential (suburbia)

Figure 9.5 Burgess concentric model

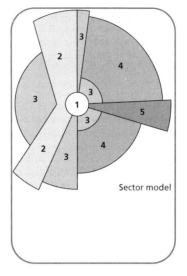

Sector model

Figure 9.6 Hoyt model

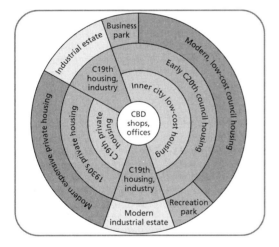

Figure 9.7 UK industrial city model

Urban change (post-1950)

Change is an important theme, which runs through many of the environment units. The syllabus mentions industry and industrial location, residential environments, traffic management, Central Business District, e.g. pedestrianisation and the impact of out of town shopping, and the linkages between these changes. We also need to consider the 'Inner City'.

A typical question is: 'Cities never sleep. There is always something happening'.

Referring to any city that you have studied in an EMDC, explain the changes that have taken place in either the CBD or in the 'inner city'. (*6 marks*)

Changes within the CBD

Over the last 20 years all our major cities in the UK have had to deal with a number of important issues, such as the growth of the menace from the motor car, changing shopping patterns, high cost of land and social problems.

Traffic

I made a mistake. I should have taken the train into Glasgow. However I drove in, a Saturday three weeks before Christmas. The new motorway, the M77, allowed me to zoom up the road and I hit the traffic jam in record time! I crawled over the Kingston Bridge into the CBD. All around me were other motorists searching for that elusive piece of space (called a parking bay). I found one. I emptied all my change and noted that the dial barely moved. However I felt elated, and fought my way around the shops, losing track of time. I came back 20 minutes late and got a parking ticket for £30. I then crawled out of the city. Great day. Mind you I got a card similar to the one I could have got back home! OK. So what is the problem? Cities existed before cars were around, with narrow streets converging at nodal points. Most of the readers of this book will be 17/18 or approaching that age. What do you want? A car of course! There are now 20 million cars in the UK, and that figure is growing. In 1900 a horse and cart travelling east to west across Glasgow moved at an average speed of 11.7 mph. In 2003, the figure was 11.4 mph. Cars take up as much space when they park, and regretfully pollute the air and cause many accidents and injuries every year. The peak demands from commuting, chaos caused from road works and the delays from buses stopping and vans unloading add to our misery. What are the solutions? The key word is management. Look at the list of points below: motorway bypass/ ring roads, new bridges, 'park and ride' schemes, 'dial a bus', improved bus, underground and train services, bus and taxi lanes, traffic free zones, yellow lines, parking metres, wardens, lights, one-way systems, fines, towing zones, multi-storey and underground car parks, vehicle congestion changes, office flexi time, and so on. We are not short of ideas. We are now increasingly discouraging people taking their cars into the city.

Questions and Answers

SAQ 9   Applying these notes, describe what your case study city is doing to manage and regulate cars in an urban area.

Answer to SAQ 9

Take your answer from the table, plus notes from an urban area that you know well.

Changing shopping patterns

We have more money than ever before, more time and greater freedom to move about and greater choice. So do we shop in the CBDs, or are we lured to the edge of city retail centres? Due to congestion, lack of space for development and increasing costs, the central business sites are becoming less popular. 'Edge of town' sites have many attractions. The problem is that growth on the fringes could well be at the expense of decline in the centre. Planning permission is required for such expansion. Objections may come from existing businesses, from people who are not so mobile, (those with no cars, some elderly people and the poor) or the existing users of the land (e.g. farmers)

The High Street or out-of-town centres?

For example, Glasgow's Argyle Street versus Braehead Shopping Centre

High street advantages and disadvantages

Traditional place to shop.
Allow us to compare shops.
Accessible with a central location, routes converge.
Has variety of other services (e.g. finance/
    recreation).
But busy and congested.
Expensive and difficult to park (parking tickets!).
Not so safe.
Lack of food shops.
Lack of space for expansion.

Out of town

Parking and accessibility by car.
Covered shopping, dry and safe.
Choice: Range of modern shops.
Convenience: One-stop shopping.
Bright attractive environment.
Often bulk savings.
Room for expansion (no parking tickets!).
But, not accessible for those without car.
Shops seem to be 'all the same'.
Put city shops out of business.

The High Street fights back!

◆ Pedestrianisation, e.g. in Argyll and Sauchiehall Streets

◆ New attractive malls, (e.g. Buchanan Galleries, St Enoch Centre) with a really pleasant shopping environment and with a good range of shops and restaurants.

◆ Street landscaping, e.g. benches, sculptures

◆ Street entertainment.

◆ The CBD has also seen a number of other specialised developments in recent years. In Glasgow, there has been a growth in the number of new building complexes (e.g. banks, insurance, finance) recreation (pubs and restaurants) and hotels/ tourism related initiatives.

So that I cannot be accused of a 'West Coast bias', let's have a look at changes in Edinburgh's CBD. Although there are planning restrictions, there are new hotels (Sheraton), new shops (Harvey Nicholls), modern shopping malls (Waverly Centre/ St. James), new and improved tourist attractions (Dynamic Earth/ National Gallery), pedestrianised roads (Rose St), and bus and taxi lanes (Princes St).

Questions and Answers

SAQ 10 Referring to any city that you have studied in an EMDC, describe and explain the changes that have taken place in the CBD. What impact have these changes had on other parts of the city? You should refer to named examples within the CBD. *(6 marks)*

Answer to SAQ 10

Check through the notes above.

Changes in the Inner City

This zone is that area of mixed housing and industry surrounding the CBD. It is sometimes called the 'zone in transition' or 'the twilight zone'. In Glasgow, following the 1950s, we had the problems of poor housing and industrial decline. This area grew at a time of massive change (19th-century industrial expansion with in-migration of labour). The city reached a population total of over 1.1 million in 1950. Since then, businesses have moved out and many people have left. By 2003 the population of the city was under 700,000.

The tenements were no more than slums. They were old, often overcrowded and lacking key facilities (inside toilets), with poor local services (schools, shops, health clinics) in an environment that was congested and polluted. The key industries had declined and unemployment added to the social decay and poverty of this 'blighted' area. There was graffiti, an ageing population, racial conflict, lack of recreational space, lack of services, road congestion, crime, air pollution, and unemployment. So what happened?

Questions and Answers

SAQ 11 Referring to any city that you have studied in an EMDC, describe and explain the problems, and comment on the changes that have been taken to 'solve the problem' of the 'inner city'. *(8 marks)*

Answer to SAQ 11

Glasgow   An answer would include reference to the following points (note that your case study city could be different; however you may well find that the points equally apply):

Comprehensive development areas created (29 of them in the city e.g. Gorbals, Govan, Partick) old buildings knocked down, people rehoused on peripheral estates (e.g. Drumchapel, Easterhouse) which sometimes became deprived zones associated with high unemployment and social problems (drugs, alcohol abuse, poverty, crime). On cleared sites, high-rise blocks were seen to be a solution. Once again there were problems, with some of the new blocks poorly designed and constructed, often lacking a community spirit and play facilities for children. Projects such as GEAR and the changing emphasis towards modernisation and renovation of tenements were viewed as successful. New Towns (such as Irvine and East Kilbride) were also successful in attracting new industry and providing housing. Other points to note. New shopping centres, health clinics, parks and open spaces created, new roads, the attraction of high profile events, (e.g. Glasgow, 'City of Culture', City of Architecture, and Garden Festival City'), new developments alongside the river (the SECC conference centre, the Armadillo, hotels, bars, casino, urban walkway, houses and flats, marina, workshops, retail and food parks, cinema and recreation complexes).

Let's not kid ourselves. Glasgow still has immense problems. However with government money, local government money, European Union grants and private initiatives the city has made an impressive start.

Suburbia

A study of Figures 9.1 to 9.3 will show that modern housing can be found at the edge of a city. This zone is sometimes referred to as 'suburbia'. There has been very substantial growth in this area over the last 50 years. Once again you could be asked to describe this zone from map evidence. Go to suburbia in Glasgow or any of the cities in the UK, and you should see the following features:

◆ Located on the outer fringes/outskirts of urban areas

◆ Expensive modern houses (often detached/semi-detached/front and rear gardens/off street parking/ garages). Low density

◆ Close to the 'green belt' (with woodland/recreation/water/farmland/parks)

◆ Room for expansion but increasing pressure and conflict/increasing value of land and costs

◆ Accessible by road for commuting into the CBD or along the modern 'ring road' network to other towns/ industrial estates/science parks)

◆ Street patterns with local roads separate from through traffic, cul-de-sacs/crescents

◆ A range of suitable services (health clinics/local convenience shops and small shopping areas/golf courses/parks and schools).

As I mentioned at the start of this unit, there is overlap between this urban environment core and the interaction, 'Urban change and its management.'

There are topics I have included here which could equally appear in an interaction question in the second paper:

◆ Housing.

◆ Change, problems and solutions in the CBD and the 'Inner City'.

◆ Traffic change, problems and solutions.

◆ Changes in shopping and the movement to the edge of the city.

◆ Redevelopment.

◆ Suburbia.

That's it. You have now reached the end of the eighth and final environment unit.

ENVIRONMENTAL INTERACTION: RURAL LAND RESOURCES

 The main idea is that rural land resources are the end product of a wide range of physical factors influenced by human factors.

Key Points

The area of study is the UK, and you are expected to have a knowledge and understanding of:

- The main features of glaciated upland, coastal and upland limestone landscapes
- The factors involved in the change over time of the landscapes
- The economic and social opportunities which the land resource provides: agriculture, forestry, energy production, tourism, mineral exploitation, industry and water storage
- The environmental problems and conflicts which arise from the competing demands
- Reasons for and the impact of UK and European Union policies affecting rural land use.

There is an overlap between some sections of the Physical Environment theme Lithosphere and this Interaction, Rural Land Resources. However this Interaction goes beyond a recognition and understanding of the three **key landscapes**: glaciated uplands, coastal and upland limestone. It is important to revise the key **features** and **processes**. Detailed review of past questions makes it clear that you need to have in-depth knowledge about one upland and one coastal land resource, set within a named area. Is there a difference between a Physical Environment theme and an Interaction question? Yes! The interaction question is structured to draw out far more detail. As you can see from the SQA syllabus above, you are also expected to understand the opportunities, the problems and conflicts within an upland and a coastal landscape.

Questions and Answers

SAQ 1   With the aid of annotated diagrams, describe and explain how the main features of a carboniferous limestone landscape were formed. Both underground and surface features should be mentioned.   *(10 marks)*

Answer to SAQ 1

The markers are looking for detail. No one expects you to create a wonderful work of art. But you must attempt some sketches. An answer without drawings would be marked out of a maximum of 7. You also need to describe and then explain. It is not possible to include details of all the limestone features, but you should draw some of the following:

Questions and Answers continued ➤

Questions and Answers continued

Answer to SAQ 1 continued

Caverns	Caves/underground lakes/rivers
Dry valleys	Gorges
Disappearing/resurgent streams	Shake holes
Stalagmites, stalactites and pillars	Limestone pavement with clints and grykes
Scars/scree	Sink/ swallow holes/potholes

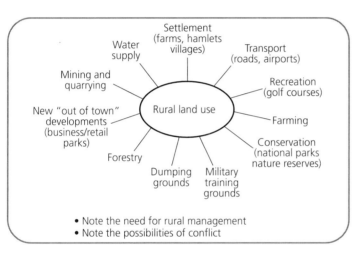

• Note the need for rural management
• Note the possibilities of conflict

There is concern and conflict over how we manage the most important resource that we have in this country. Figure 10.1 summarises many of these key rural land uses

Figure 10.1 Rural land resource management

Questions and Answers

SAQ 2 The Lake District and the Cairngorms are particularly noted for glaciated scenery. For either of these two areas or any other named glaciated upland area in the UK explain, with the aid of annotated diagrams, how the main features of the physical landscape were formed.   *(10 marks)*

Answer to SAQ 2

In some ways my guidance notes are similar to SAQ 1, but in this question you need to have some detailed knowledge about your named area. If your answer is vague, then once again you will get no more than 7 marks. For example, if you are writing about the Lake District you could name particular corries (e.g. Stickle Tarn) or an arête (e.g. Striding Edge). In terms of detail, you would be expected to write for about 15 to 20 minutes on such a question. As far as the content is concerned, you should again select from the list of well-known glaciated mountain features. Note again the importance of drawing diagrams. Check back to the summary of features listed within the lithosphere section.

The Changing Shape of our Coastline

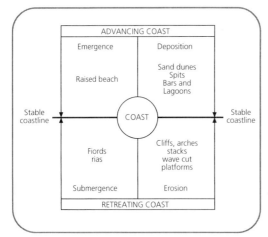

Figure 10.2 Classification of coasts

Read the following note and study Figure 10.2, which is a 'classification of coasts'. A study of old maps and records reveals a picture of change. (You can check back to your coast notes in the environment unit, 'lithosphere'.)

Summary

Retreating erosion

The coastline is being eroded as a result of the action of the sea. The key features formed include cliffs, arches, stacks and wave-cut platforms.

Retreating submergence

During the last ice age, a great weight of ice caused the crust to buckle and be depressed. The melting of vast quantities of ice caused the level of the sea to rise, flooding low-lying coastlines and valleys. (See Figure 10.3). A **fiord** (**fjord**) was formed where glaciers eroded down below sea level. When the ice melted, the sea level rose, flooding the valley. **Rias** are drowned river valleys, tributaries and estuaries in non-glaciated areas.

Advancing deposition

Some coastlines are subject to deposition by sand, mud, shingle and pebbles. These coastlines have features such as beaches, sand dunes, spit, bars and lagoons.

Advancing emergence

After the melting of the ice sheets and glaciers over the UK, the crust started to 'bounce' back. This process is called isostacy. The end result was that land 'emerged' from the sea. Around the coastline of Scotland you find many examples of '**raised beaches**'.

Questions and Answers

SAQ 3 With the aid of annotated diagrams, describe and explain the formation of the main features of

either   a coastline of deposition

or   a coastline of erosion   *(6 marks)*

Answer to SAQ 3

This has been covered in the lithosphere environment unit and in the text above.

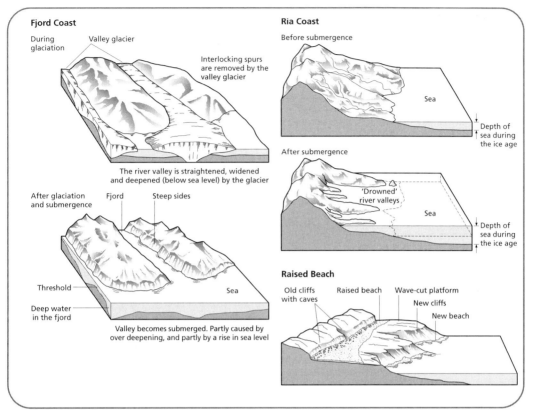

Figure 10.3 Fiord, Rias and raised beach processes and coastal types

National Parks

You need to have an understanding of opportunities, problems and conflict within a protected area. This section will focus on National Parks. We have 12 NPs in England and Wales, (the original 10, plus the Norfolk Broads and the New Forest*) and now 2 in Scotland (Loch Lomond and the Trossachs, and the Cairngorms). The areas were selected since they offered outstanding landscape features, an environment under pressure worthy of conservation and required to be managed to reduce the conflict and to protect the 'national interest'. Of course, NPs are neither 'national' nor 'parks' in the conventional sense! Unlike the American NPs, the land within a UK NP is not all owned by the Government. Our parks are not 'open air museums'. People live, work, quarry, farm, holiday and grow trees in these areas.

The 1949 National Parks Act, created National Park Authorities whose task was to

◆ protect and enhance the landscape

◆ encourage and assist the public to take part in outdoor recreational activities, while protecting the social and economic life of people who live within the parks.

Who owns the land?

Selected parks and ownership (*Designated June 2004)

Selected Park	Forestry Commission	NPA, Nat. Trust Eng. Heritage	Water	Ministry of Defence (MOD)	Local Authority	Private Farming
Northumberland	19%	1%	1%	23%	less than 1%	56%
Lake District	6	28	7	0	less than 1%	59
Dartmoor	2	22	4	14	less than 1%	57
Yorkshire Dales	0	3	0.5	0.5	less than 1%	96
Overall (12 NPs)	10	8	4	7	less than 1%	71

Questions and Answers

SAQ 4   Using the information from the table above, explain why the pattern of land ownership in NPs may make their management difficult.   *(5 marks)*

Answer to SAQ 4

You should use some of the figures from the table, but be careful not to overdo it.

- Note the very small percentage owned by the NPA themselves.
- Note the high percentage owned by private landowners (mainly farmers) in an area such as the Yorkshire Dales; the number would be measured in thousands of owners. Clearly this makes it difficult if not impossible to seek out a common shared and agreed viewpoint.
- Note the presence of some other mighty powerful interest groups with their own specific interests. For example the MOD on Dartmoor; when they wish to roll out the tanks for an exercise no one will stop them! Other users include the Water Boards and the Forestry Commission. Once again it is difficult to have an influence over these single interest groups.

Why are the NPs so popular?

Always beware of statistics, but some poor soul has calculated that in 2002 there were 120 million 'visitor days' spent in the National Parks. Now try and work out that one!

Questions and Answers

SAQ 5 Describe and suggest why National Parks attract widely differing numbers of visitors. You should refer to Figure 10.4. *(8 marks)*

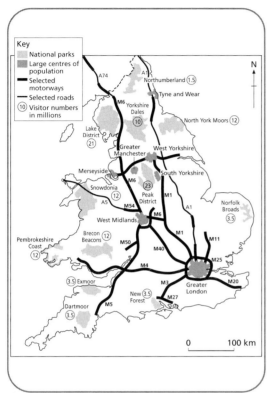

Answer to SAQ 5

The overall total number of days is around 120 million, varying from over 20 million in the 'big' two, the Lake District and the Peak District, down to figures of around 1–3 million in Northumberland, Norfolk and the New Forest. The NPs in the North of England and Wales appear to attract more visitors. In between we have the North York Moors (12 million) and Snowdonia (12 million). You do actually get marks for stating the obvious! In this question about 3 marks (maximum) would be allocated for description.

Explanation. What are the clues on the map? You have been given data on the location of the parks, the main urban population concentrations, and selected motorways and main roads. The key points:

Figure 10.4 National Parks, visitor numbers and accessibility

Answer to SAQ 5 continued

◆ 90 per cent of all visits take place in cars and people are prepared to travel up to 2-3 hours for a 'day trip', so make reference to the location of the main urban centres.

◆ The road network allows people to travel a considerable distance quickly. The Peak District is relatively close to the West Midlands, West and South Yorkshire, Manchester and Merseyside. The M1 and M6 motorways open up a very sizeable 'catchment' area. Even the more geographically remote Dartmoor can be reached from the West Midlands and London relatively quickly along the M5 and M4 motorways. The less 'popular' parks, e.g. the Norfolk Broads and Northumberland, are more remote from the main urban centres and have weaker motorway links.

◆ The parks do vary in 'pulling power'. For example the spectacular scenery in the Lake District, with plenty of opportunities for outdoor activities, may be more appealing than the 'atmospheric' and historic Northumberland moors.

HOW TO PASS HIGHER GEOGRAPHY

Social and Economic Opportunities

This is one of the key areas within this topic. Looking back over past Higher questions, there has scarcely been a year when there has not been a question about the social and economic opportunities presented from the landscapes. You need to have knowledge about 2 case study landscapes. You must have details on 1 upland area (either glaciated or limestone) and one coastal area. The choice is yours.

The structure adopted below is that I shall identify a number of general social and economic themes that you could mention and then have a look at a worked answer from a recent question. You can then attempt a couple of questions yourself.

There are opportunities for people to earn a living and have a decent quality of life in such areas.

I would suggest that there are 6 main headings that could be relevant: **Agriculture, Industry and mineral exploitation, Energy production, Forestry, Tourism, Water storage**

When putting together data for your case study I suggest that you take notes under these headings. It is unlikely that your examples will have relevant entries under all six headings.

Agriculture Sheep farming on the less fertile upland slopes. Farmers can rent out fields for caravans and camping. There will be decent pasture for beef and dairy cattle on the valley floor and lower slopes, Hunting and fishing may also be found on farmland.

Energy production Hydro electric power can be generated making use of environment features such as high precipitation, hard impermeable rocks, glaciated valleys and hanging valleys, all ideal for creating the lakes and dams for power. The coastal waters may also allow for the generation of power from the waves, and the upland moors are perfect for wind farms.

Tourism The environment is perfect for both active (e.g. walking, pony trekking, winter sports, rock climbing) and passive (e.g. driving, sightseeing, picnicking) activities. The varied landscapes (mountains, moors, coasts, limestone, glaciated, lakes) attract millions of visitors. There are opportunities for employment in hotels, and B and Bs, cafes, museums and shops.

There will be improvements to the local infrastructure that will help to keep rural populations in place and villages alive. There will be an injection of money into the local economy.

Industry and mineral exploitation

Minerals such as copper, limestone (for building, cement, industrial and agricultural limestone) and gritstone (for roads/ runways) are examples of rocks exploited. Associated with such developments will be demands to improve transport facilities.

Forestry Upland landscapes are not always suitable for agriculture. However in the slightly higher, sheltered, drained yet less fertile land, trees can be grown for profit.

Water storage While there are not many job opportunities, lakes have been created as reservoirs for drinking water, recreation and nature reserves. Such lakes may also attract recreation and tourist related activities.

What would the standard question look like?

Questions and Answers

SAQ 6 'For any named upland or coastal area of the UK you have studied, explain the main social and economic opportunities.' *(8 marks)*

Have a shot at SAQ 6 now. The key is being able to use these headings and apply the question to a named area.

Answer to SAQ 6

Study area: a coastal area, the Ayrshire coast between Troon and Turnberry.

This coastal strip has a variety of landforms. There are sandy beaches, river mouths and cliffs. Almost 80,000 people live along this stretch, and include the settlements of Troon, Prestwick, Ayr and Maidens.

The flat land adjacent to the coast has presented little in the way of difficulty for the development of roads, railways and the international airport at Prestwick.

This stretch of coastline between Troon and Turnberry offers economic and social opportunities under the headings of: agriculture, industry and mineral exploitation, tourism.

Agriculture

The low-lying, damp, mild winter conditions favour the growth of pasture (with dairy farming) and the cultivation of early potatoes. Altitude and steepness of slope are the only physical problems holding back farming in some areas.

Industry and Mineral exploitation

The main settlements of Ayr and Prestwick have a number of service and food-based industries. The main service occupations are linked to tourism and recreation. The area was formerly an important coalmining and quarrying area, but little now remains of that industry. Hard basalt rock for road surfacing is quarried within the area. Ayr and Troon are long established ports. Both are not as busy as they once were. Troon is the terminal for the Seacat to Ireland, with a fish market and home to a fishing fleet, and Ayr is principally involved trading coal to Ireland.

Tourism

The coastline has been very important for the development of golf courses. The two Open Championship courses (Troon and Turnberry) and all the other coastal courses attract many people from all over the world. Jobs, income and improvements to local services are the benefits. The coastal scenery at Culzean and the historic castle (now owned and managed by the National Trust for Scotland) is popular with locals and tourists. Other attractions include the race course in Ayr, nature trails, a holiday camp, caravan parks, bird watching, sea fishing, a cycle path, marinas and sailing clubs, urban parks and the historical cultural attractions associated with Robert Burns. The long sandy beach from Troon to Ayr has been a 'magnet' for holidaymakers for over 100 years.

Questions and *Answers* continued ➤

Questions *and Answers* continued

Answer to SAQ 6 continued

There are some problems. Work has to be done to protect the sand dunes along the beach and at the golf courses in Troon. Much of the tourism related work is seasonal and the traditional 'seaside' based holiday at the beach in Ayrshire has almost died a death, due to the attractions of the Mediterranean.

Summary of problems and benefits of tourism

Summary

Benefits

- Employment (e.g. 7,500 people working within the National Parks of England and Wales)
- The average amount spend per day is £10 per person. With over 120 million day visits to NPs, you can work out what it adds up to.
- Farmers forced to diversify and look for alternative sources of income.
- Local services may well disappear if it were not for the tourists and day visitors.
- Historic buildings have been renovated and opened for tourists.
- Ancient crafts and local traditions can be kept alive for the tourists.

Problems

- 'Honey pot' sites with too many people in the most attractive and accessible places, resulting in congestion.
- Footpath erosion with thousands of feet killing the plants and eroding the soil.
- Disturbance to wildlife in their natural habitat caused by walkers, mountain bikers.
- Large numbers of people inevitably means large amounts of litter.
- Damage to farmland with the trampling of crops, gates left open and dogs running wild.
- Loss of services as more and more shops are focused on tourists rather than local people.

Questions *and Answers*

SAQ 7   Study the sketch of a glaciated upland area (Figure 10.5), based on a Lake District view, and annotate it using the 'conflict and problem' points given.

The answer should be fairly obvious!

The value of this question is that it allows you to identify a number of problems and conflicts that can arise in an area such as this. The whole idea of conflict is that different users have their own priorities how an area should be. Look back at Diagram 10.1. Pick out any grouping of land uses, and try to identify the possible conflicts, eg *dumping* and *recreation*.

Questions and *Answers* continued ➤

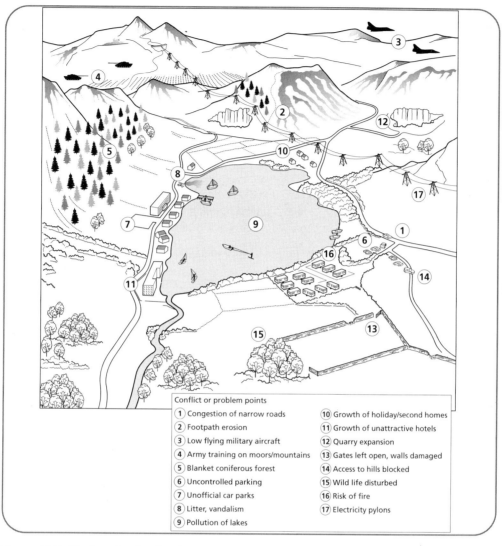

Conflict or problem points

1. Congestion of narrow roads
2. Footpath erosion
3. Low flying military aircraft
4. Army training on moors/mountains
5. Blanket coniferous forest
6. Uncontrolled parking
7. Unofficial car parks
8. Litter, vandalism
9. Pollution of lakes
10. Growth of holiday/second homes
11. Growth of unattractive hotels
12. Quarry expansion
13. Gates left open, walls damaged
14. Access to hills blocked
15. Wild life disturbed
16. Risk of fire
17. Electricity pylons

Figure 10.5 Glaciated upland, Lake District

Questions and Answers continued   ❓

SAQ 8   Select an upland area or a coastal area in the UK that you have studied and describe and explain any two conflicts that have occurred.   *(6 marks)*

Answer to SAQ 8

The marker can mark 2/4, 3/3, 4/2. Of course, you need to select your own study areas. Here is one example of conflict.

Study area: The lower slopes of Ben Lomond and Loch Lomond

Conflict: Commercial forestry

Questions and *Answers* continued ➤

HOW TO PASS HIGHER GEOGRAPHY

Questions and Answers continued

Answer to SAQ 8 continued

Some people believe that forestry adds to the beauty of the loch and the slopes around Ben Lomond across to Loch Katrine, and that the industry provides jobs in rural communities such as Balmaha. Trees can stabilise the soil and hold back floodwater. Scottish wildlife thrives in the woodlands and the area is very popular with visitors who walk, climb, picnic and relax in the area. Not everyone shares this view. When the slopes are covered in bleak identical coniferous trees, the landscape is considered unattractive and not natural. Very few jobs are created and the trees can block walkers' access onto the hills. It takes up to 40 years to make a decent financial return from a forest, and more jobs and more money may be generated from sheep farms, grouse, fishing and other developments.

It is possible to reach a compromise, but don't expect everyone to be happy.

Study area: Dartmoor

Conflict: Military activities

The army and air force need to train and exercise over difficult and testing land. The area in Dartmoor is perfect with the rugged moors, bleak landscape, poor visibility and harsh weather. Where better to test out the army? The barren moors are also perfect for testing out equipment, whether it is planes, helicopters, tanks or guns. The problem is that locals and visitors can be denied access to the moors at certain times, and that roads can be choked with the army vehicles. There is a problem with noise and low-flying planes can disturb animals.

I would suggest that you identify another couple of examples of conflict or problems from your case study of coastal and upland areas.

The final task is to seek out solutions. This is what makes the study of Geography relevant to real life. We are not content to simply describe and identify problems. We go on to suggest solutions and analyse the impact of all the changes that we make. Take each of the problems identified around Figure 10.5, and jot down what you would consider to be an obvious 'common sense' solution.

Have a look at SAQ 9 below. The markers have a degree of freedom in how they mark this question. For full marks, all three parts must be tackled. A minimum of 2 marks has to be awarded for any part and a maximum of 5 for another part. The problem with this question is making sure that you write enough detail. You have the time to develop your answer.

The Government, European Union and the Countryside

In an attempt to cut down farm surpluses and to protect or conserve the countryside, the government and the European Union have introduced a number of initiatives.

A study of the examination has indicated that 6 schemes have been mentioned in SQA question over the last 10 or so years.

Questions and Answers

SAQ 9 Referring to a named upland or named coastal area you have studied in detail,

a) Describe the benefits which tourism has brought.

b) Give examples of land use conflicts or problems which have arisen.

c) Describe the measures taken to resolve or reduce those conflicts.
(12 marks)

Answer to SAQ 9

Both parts a and b have been covered above.

Most of the measures taken to resolve conflict involve **planning** and **control**.

◆ Restrict access to certain areas, ban vehicles, introduce park and ride schemes, build new roads and by-passes (e.g. Peak District NP).

◆ Employ wardens and volunteer guides (all NPs).

◆ Prevent walkers from eroding paths by paving paths and controlling access (All NPs).

◆ Use legislation to prevent inappropriate development of housing, camp sites and industry

◆ Around quarries, screen the development, restore and landscape the site after use, control the access points for lorries, open railway tracks (Peak District).

◆ To resolve bleak forest views, plant mixed deciduous trees, construct access paths and roads, and allow people to picnic and walk in the woods (Snowdonia).

◆ Control use at the honey-pot sites by encouraging development at a small number of locations. The idea is that most people will focus on such points. Construct car parks, toilets, nature trails, shops, and cafes, information centres with wardens (all NPs).

◆ Control speed of boats on the water, create 'swimmers only' zones and fine polluters (Lake District)

◆ When house prices are rising it is possible for the local authorities to provide low-cost housing for locals

◆ Educate the public to enjoy, conserve and protect the upland and coastal landscapes (study Geography!)

Key Words

★ **Environmentally Sensitive Areas (ESAs)** ★ **EU Farm Production Quotas** ★ **Less Favoured Areas (LFAs)** ★ **Set Aside Land** ★ **Farm Diversification Grants (FDGs)** ★ **Woodland Grant Scheme/ Farm Woodland Scheme**

In the UK we are part of the European Union's Common Agricultural Policy (CAP)

HOW TO PASS HIGHER GEOGRAPHY

Questions and Answers (?)

SAQ 10 Select any three of the schemes listed above.

Describe their aims and comment on the impact on the rural landscape
(9 marks)

Answer to SAQ 10

Set Aside Land

Since 1992 the European Union has required some farmers to 'set aside' up to 15% of their land for a period of 5 years. In return compensation payments are made, and the fields are left in fallow. This is to control overproduction of cereals. It is expensive to store and transport surplus crops, and it actually works out cheaper to give the farmer money to grow nothing! The policy is not to destroy surplus food. This takes land out of production and encourages diversification of crop.

Farm Diversification Grants (FDGs)

Available since 1998. Support is given to activities that are non agricultural, and will widen out use of rural areas. It includes recreational use, golf courses, adventure activities, educational farms, farm shops, mountain biking, trout farms and traditional craft schools.

There are problems such as noise, litter, damage to the land, disruption to the 'traditional' rural way of life.

EU Farm Production Quotas

We are able to produce more and more food each year. There is only so much milk that we can drink! The EU and the government set a limit that cannot be exceeded by a farm. Farmers receive a set price for their product. We need to cut back so that we do not overproduce and flood the market with any crop or product. If this happens prices become too low and we have the embarrassment of having to 'dump' the surplus. Farmers complain that their income is reduced. This has forced them to think about other ways in which they can diversify by choice of crop grown or introducing new activities

Environmentally Sensitive Areas (ESAs)

This attempts to encourage farmers to have a more sensitive approach to farming and farmland. Financial grants are available to conserve/ enhance the landscape: e.g. create dry stone walls, wildlife habitats, woodland walks; protect archaeological sites and historic features; maintain grassland; limit use of pesticides, insecticides, fertilisers and plant hedgerows.

This has been very successful and copied throughout the EU.

Less Favoured Areas (LFAs)

This initiative tends to be located in the more 'isolated' regions, such as the Western Highlands and Islands, such as on Skye and Harris. The problem of rural depopulation and unemployment can be tackled through grants and loans which support farming (draining land) and tourism (reconstructing piers and jetties, roads).

Woodland Grant Scheme/ Farm Woodland Scheme

The Woodland Grant (1991) encourages replanting of broadleaved woodland, and the Farm Woodland Scheme (1988) encouraged farmers to plant/ maintain woodland through grants. Since 1988 over 50 million trees have been planted. This provides shelter, recreational opportunities, wildlife habitat enhancement and a source of timber for the future.

ENVIRONMENTAL INTERACTION: RIVER BASIN MANAGEMENT

Key Points

Within river basins, water control projects are undertaken for a variety of reasons and on a range of scales. These projects are examples of human interference with systems, especially hydrological systems. The changes often have both beneficial and adverse consequences.

You need to have detailed knowledge of one river basin from Africa or North America or Asia.

River Basins

Simply stated, this is the area drained by a river and its tributaries.

Questions and Answers

SAQ 1   Describe the general pattern of river basins in North America, Asia or Africa. (Usually there is a large-scale map to assist you.)   *(5 marks)*

Answer to SAQ 1

Africa

There are a handful of river basins shown. Note the lack of drainage in North Africa (Sahara Desert) with the Nile the only major system draining north to the Mediterranean. The White Nile drains from Lake Victoria and the Blue Nile is fed from the Ethiopian Mountains. In Central Africa, the Volta, Niger Benue and Zaire (Congo) Rivers drain south and westwards into the Atlantic Ocean and the Gulf of Guinea. This area has high levels of precipitation (although the savanna lands have a seasonal pattern). In South Africa, the Zambezi and Limpopo Rivers drain into the Indian Ocean. All of these river systems have major water project schemes.

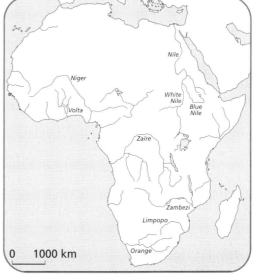

Figure 12.1 Major River Basin, Africa

Now have a shot at answering the question for North America.

Questions and *Answers* continued ➤

Questions *and* Answers *continued*

Answer to SAQ 1 *continued*

North America

The largest basin, bounded by the Rockies to the west and the Appalachians to the east, includes the Mississippi, Missouri and the Tennessee rivers drain southwards to the Gulf of Mexico. The basins of the Columbia and the Colorado are smaller due to the watershed of the continent running down the Rocky Mountain chain. The Mackenzie system drains northwards to the Arctic Ocean with the large area of the Canadian Shield draining into Hudson Bay. The main easterly basin covers the Great Lakes and the St Laurence River, which drains towards the Atlantic.

Figure 12.2 Major River Basin, North America

Hydrological Cycle

This process can also appear as a question in the Physical Environment unit, Hydrosphere. You are expected to be able to apply that knowledge to the impact that major river basin developments can have upon the cycle. Refer back to Figure 3.1.

Questions *and* Answers

SAQ 2   Remind yourself of the meaning of: Evaporation, Condensation, Precipitation, Transpiration, Evapotranspiration, Groundwater, Run-off, Storage.

Check your answers from diagram 3.1

SAQ 3   Describe the hydrological cycle.

(Note that you could also be asked to draw the Hydrological Cycle, showing the main processes, transfers and stages.)

Answer to SAQ 3

Essentially earth is approximately 71% water. Of that total 97% is salt water found in the oceans and seas. The remaining 3% is fresh water. The bulk of that is locked up in the icecaps. In total only 0.76% of the total amount of water is in a form and location that is

Questions and *Answers* continued ➤

Questions and Answers continued

Answer to SAQ 3 continued

available to people and to move through the hydrological cycle. This water is in our rivers, lakes and within the soil and ground. The demand for water on earth has doubled over the last 20 years, and probably will do so again in the next 20. You can easily work out how this water is in demand: domestic use (drinking, washing, flushing and bathing), industry and farming, navigation, recreation and power generation. Not only do we need to manage this resource, we also need to make sure that we do not create shortages or prevent the resource from diminishing as a result of pollution.

One of the themes that runs through this unit is that of interference by 'man' with a physical system. We have chosen to try to improve on 'nature'. This interference tends to focus on the run-off and storage phases. Human interference in the hydrological cycle is not new, but we seem to be more ambitious and grand in the scale of things. The scale of the Three Gorges Project in China is a perfect example of our thinking. In arid areas with little in the way of rivers, ground storage schemes may result in large amounts of water being removed through widespread use of wells and boreholes. Over time the water table level will be lowered.

Questions and Answers

SAQ 4 Describe and explain the ways in which water control projects may change the hydrological cycle of a river basin. *(5 marks)*

This is a typical question, having appeared in more or less this form in 6 out of the last 11 years. It is worth noting that large-scale water management projects involve damming back a river, constructing a barrier or dam, controlling the level of the water and constructing irrigation and drainage systems.

While this particular question does not always ask you to name any water control projects, it is always a good idea to supply that little bit of extra detail. Have a shot, then look at the answer given and note how the exam marker would have judged it.

Answer to SAQ 4

The surface run-off is reduced **(½)** with less water flowing in the river below the dam and into the sea **(½)**. While there is less evaporation from the river **(½)**, there is more evaporation from the surface of the reservoir **(½)**. Large lakes create their own microclimates **(½)**, possibly by keeping surrounding land cooler or even increasing precipitation **(½)**. Infiltration rates into the ground may be altered following the amount of water held in reservoirs **(½)**, diverted rivers or in irrigation channels **(½)**. Seasonal variations in the river levels will be altered **(½)**. Water table levels will also change **(½)**.

Full marks!

Questions and Answers

(The selection of a site for a dam)

SAQ 5 With reference to any river basin you have studied in North America, Africa or Asia, describe and explain the human and physical factors that have to be considered when selecting sites for dams and their associated reservoirs. *(5 marks)*

Answer to SAQ 5

Over the last 11 years this question has appeared no fewer than 8 times!

Think about what a dam is supposed to do.

The Three Gorges dam (2.3 km wide) across the Yangtze, when completed in 2009, will be the largest in the world, holding back a 600 km long reservoir. What are the physical and human factors that need to be considered?

Physical factors

You obviously need a solid foundation on which to construct a dam. Igneous rocks such as granite or hard metamorphic rocks provide the necessary support. It is best not to build across an earthquake fault line (!). To prevent seepage from below the dam and the flooded lake, it is best to make sure that the ground rock is not permeable or porous. To reduce costs, it makes sense to select a narrow valley across which the dam will be built.

A deep valley would also allow a deep lake to contain floodwater, and the smaller surface area would reduce evaporation. It also helps to be in an area with sufficient catchment potential. You need rain or snowmelt. In China, the Three Gorges Project involves a dam 185 metres high, 2,300 metres wide, creating a lake 600 kms long.

Human factors

You need to consider the impact of the dam and the flooded valley. For example, how much farmland would be lost; and how many people would have to be resettled. For example, at the Three Gorges site, over 1.2 million people were forced to move. This will affect the cost of the scheme. You need to consider the impact of any historical sites that would be lost. For example, on the Nile at Aswan many ancient Egyptians temples were to lost. Along the Gorge 1,300 archaeological sites will be moved or flooded; 27,000 hectares of farmland and orchards, and 19 cities will be inundated. You need to also consider accessibility for workers (although in most cases migrant labour is brought in). You should also consider the sensitivities of native cultures (e.g. native American burial sites). The distance to urban and farming communities should be considered for HEP and irrigation purposes.

You need to have detailed knowledge of one river basin from either Africa or North America or Asia.

A study of past questions will show that every year since 1993 there has been a question that requires such knowledge and understanding. A reminder of what you need to know

◆   The need for the water storage basin project and management

♦ The social, economic, political and environmental benefits of the river basin project

♦ The adverse consequences of water control projects on the selected basin and solutions

Multi-purpose river basin management schemes have been seen to be an answer to water problems around the world. The four issues are:

Water supply Flood control Hydro-electric power Navigation

The need for water management schemes

Hints and Tips

Often the question will have a number of diagrams and graphs for a particular scheme. Usually the question will offer you an alternative. You could be asked a question about a particular scheme, or you could select one of your choice. The problem with the former is that when you get a question you will see maps graphs or diagrams, that may be unfamiliar to you. What do you do? There is no need to panic! The key is to be aware of the general points below. They could be applied to almost any project in N America, Africa or Asia. You then apply these points (as far as you can) to the example given. Let's have a look at those basic features.

Questions and Answers

SAQ 5 Select a named river basin (from North America, Africa or Asia) and explain why there was a need for that water management project. *(6 marks)*

Answer to SAQ 5

This book cannot provide a full set of detailed notes. You should have studied one or more schemes in detail in class. Check through those notes now.

My answer would include reference to the following:

♦ Low annual rainfall total

♦ An unreliable rainfall pattern or a seasonal imbalance

♦ The possibility and/or need for transfer of water from an area with a water surplus to a deficit area (by aqueduct, canal or river)

♦ The need to reduce the likelihood of flooding (from seasonal precipitation or snowmelt)

♦ To provide a regular water supply for expanding urban areas, industry and agriculture (irrigation)

♦ To generate hydro-electric power (HEP) for industry, farms and communities

♦ To raise general standard of living in an area and help to reduce poverty

♦ To improve the navigation potential.

Questions and Answers continued ➤

Questions and Answers continued

SAQ 6 Study Figure 12.3, which shows water control projects in Central Valley, California, and rainfall graphs for selected stations. Describe and explain the need for water management   *(6 marks)*

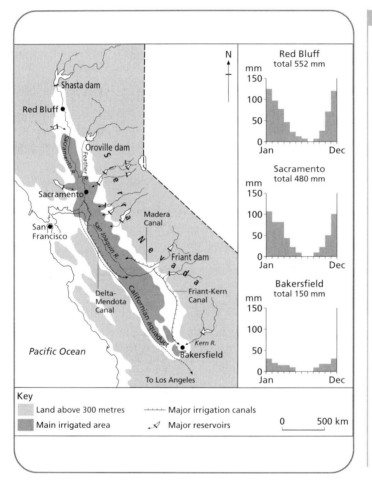

Answer to SAQ 6

◆ You could note the very low desert precipitation level in Bakersfield (150 mm per year).

◆ There is a general seasonal imbalance with a drought in the summer months in Red Bluff, Sacramento and Bakersfield (e.g. in Sacramento, less than 25 mms of rain falls between June to September).

◆ There is the possibility of transferring water from the wetter north to the drier south (down the Sacramento River/Feather River, and along the Delta Mendota canal).

Figure 12.3 Central Valley, California

◆ Snowmelt from the surrounding mountains may caused flooding in spring from the Sacramento and the San Joaquin Rivers.

◆ The main valley is flat and has the potential for further irrigation.

◆ The population of California is growing, so water will be needed for the growing cities (e.g. Los Angeles).

◆ There will be increasing demand for HEP for settlement, industry and farms.

The social, economic, political and environmental benefits and adverse consequences of a river basin project

This is the big question! A review of the past papers will show that this is core knowledge. You need to master one management project. What I shall do is provide you with the master set of key points. You should be able to apply those points to your selected project. I shall then provide you with some summary notes about the largest project being constructed at the moment, the Three Gorges in China.

You may well have studied other projects in Africa, N America or Asia.

Key Points

Benefits/Advantages	Adverse features/Disadvantages
Social	**Social**
Assists to stop rural depopulation (Damodar Valley, India).	Forced movement and resettlement of people affected by construction.
Increased food supply, reducing chance of famine (Nile).	Compensation not always paid to displaced people (Ilisu, Turkey).
New improved housing after relocation (Three Gorges, China).	Increased chance of certain diseases (bilharzia in Ghana, malaria in Mali, Senegal River).
Reduced deaths and damage from flooding (Tennessee Valley).	Communities forced to be split, and traditional way of life destroyed.
Increase in electricity availability, improving quality of life, increased recreational and recreation opportunities (California).	Loss of farmland.
Less disease (e.g. cholera, typhoid and better health, clean water, more food) (Zambezi).	Nile valley flooded for Aswan Dam, people forced to move to higher ground; burial sites, villages and fields flooded.
Growing populations can be supported. (40 million people drink water from the Colorado River).	
Economic	**Economic**
Possibility of food surpluses, double cropping, new cash crops introduced, increased yields. Increase in land suitable for irrigation and increase output (Nile, Three Gorges).	Jobs often do not go to local people. Huge costs ($1.5 billion in Turkey) for dams, HEP, pumping stations, flood control, irrigation, and infrastructure).
Money economy established (Damodar, India).	Dependence on overseas aid, and massive debts.
HEP allowing industrial development with jobs, money and exports.	More money needed to be spent to sustain project (e.g. fertilisers).

Key Points continued ➢

Key Points *continued*

Economic (continued)

Employment opportunities created in tourism, fishing, construction (China).
Allow the river to be used for year-round navigation (boats carry cargo, local people and tourists) (Tennessee).
Improve communications (e.g. roads across dam, ferries) (Nile, Colorado).

Environmental

New habitats created, especially around the dam and reservoir.
Scenery improved (e.g. attractive lake landscape).
Fresh water improves sanitation and health.
Damage from flooding reduced.
Water in the river downstream now generally at the same level.

Political

Encourages co-operation and partnerships (e.g. USA/Mexico).
Political co-operation (e.g. the Nile Basin agreement between Egypt and Sudan).
Costs can be shared between countries.

Economic (continued)

Often results in the rich becoming richer and the poor remaining poor.
Increased food often exported and not available for locals.
With loss of historic sites tourism may decrease.
Existing communication routes may be disrupted.

Environmental

Increased erosion downstream and along the coast (e.g. Nile).
Silting of the reservoirs (Volta dams with life of 80–100 years).
Increased water pollution from farming, industry and settlement.
Loss of alluvium deposited downstream.
Overwatering resulting in waterlogging and increased salinity.
High evaporation resulting in water loss (25% of water lost through evaporation in the Colorado).
Overuse of the available water (e.g. the Colorado dries up).
Increased soil erosion on riverbanks below dam.
Threat to wildlife with loss of habitats (e.g. Nile Delta) Offshore fishing affected.
Micro climatic changes and the hydrological cycle altered.

Political

Problems over how to allocate water resources and costs.
Problems over dealing with pollution.
Complex legislation to solve disputes.
Countries seriously falling out over water disputes (e.g. Turkey and Iraq and Syria are in dispute over water flow, cause of power cuts and threats to faming).

Questions and Answers

SAQ 7 Study Figures 12.4 and 12.5, climatic data and information showing River Nile discharge.

a) Describe and account for the pattern of river flow before the dam was built.

b) Describe the ways in which the river's flow has changed since the completion of the dam. *(7 marks)*

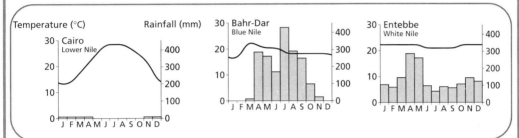

Figure 12.4

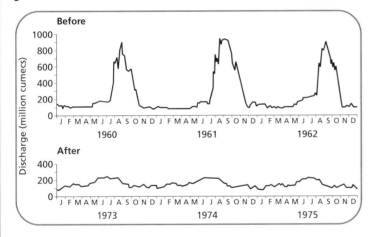

Figure 12.5

Answer to SAQ 7

I shall provide you with some notes to help you make sense of the data.

Note that the marker has 7 marks to award. He/ she can award the marks 5,4 or 3 to part a, and the balance to part b.

Note that Figure 12.4 shows the climatic regime at three sites along the course of the Nile.

Note that river discharge in Figure 12.5 is measured in 'cumecs'.

a) A description of the river discharge before the building of the dam reveals a regular pattern emerging, with a base low of around 100 to 150 cumecs most years from November to April/ May, followed by a gentle increase through May to July (200 to 250 cumecs). There then follows a dramatic increase each year during July to September and then an equally dramatic decline (reaching a peak discharge of 900 cumecs).

Questions and *Answers* continued ➤

Questions *and* Answers *continued*

Answer to SAQ 7 continued

The Cairo climatic data does not really provide any clues. At Bahr Dar, the seasonal precipitation will cause the pronounced rise in the Nile discharge. There is a small time lapse, since it will take a few weeks before this heavy summer precipitation reaches the Nile, north of Aswan. (Heaviest precipitation is in July, river reaches peak in late August/September.) Note that the Blue and White Niles merge. The Blue Nile is seasonal, while the White Nile rises in the Lake Victoria area, where rainfall is less seasonal. The more regular equatorial rainfall at Entebbe means that there is a fairly steady volume in the river all year.

b) This question is relatively easy. Describe the changes since the completion of the dam. The extremes no longer exist, and the flow is generally even and more or less regular throughout the seasons. The flow does vary slightly from 100 to 225 cumecs. If you were to be asked to explain this change, then you would refer to the dam holding back floodwater, and controlling the release of the water. The slight summer maximum would possibly be for downstream irrigation and the need to lower the lake level at the Aswan Dam.

Example

Three Gorges Case Study, Yangtze River China
'He who controls the water, controls the people' – Chinese saying.

This massive project is in the process of being constructed and will not be completed for a number of years. The textbooks are obviously incomplete, so how do you get the necessary information. There have been TV programmes and articles in papers and magazines, presenting the contrasting arguments for and against such a project. If you have access to the Internet at home, a library or at school, then you can quickly get into the debate. Construction began in 1994 and should be complete by 2009. The reservoir will be 1.1 km wide, 600 km long and will store 40 billion cubic metres (Picture that then!) The new surface of the lake will be 175 metres above the existing level of the Yangtze River. The key functions of this project are flood control, power generation and improved navigation.

Benefits/Advantages	Adverse features/Disadvantages
'A triumph of human determination and ingenuity'	**'A mammoth folly, a triumph of ego and political showmanship'**
Social	*Social*
Will end the threat and damage from flooding	19 cities, 140 towns and 1,350 villages to be flooded (numbers vary according to the source). 1.2–1.9million people to be resettled. Massive social and human upheaval. Promises made regarding resettlement and compensation may not be
Will improve quality of life for millions with electricity in homes and farms. People will be compensated for the loss of their homes and farmland. Promise of	

Example *continued* ➤

Example *continued*

Benefits/Advantages	Adverse features/Disadvantages

Benefits/Advantages

Social continued
better houses, better jobs, improvements in health and education. 15 million people downstream free from threat of flooding. Annual flood risk cut from 10% to 1%. Should end rural depopulation.

Economic
Massive power stations and 26 generators producing 18 megawatts for industry, farming and homes. Increase in shipping estimated to be from 10 million tons to 50 million. Transport costs cut by 35%. Ships reach 1,500 miles from the coast. Jobs and a money economy will boost output and promote trade.

Environmental
Saving of 40 million tons of coal a year. Reduction in greenhouse gas emissions, creating a clean environmentally friendly area, with new areas reclaimed. Land degradation halted. The waters on the river safer for navigation.

Political
This massive project is symbolic signature to the world that China is an international power. Has encouraged trade and financial links. Government proud that this is the largest such project in the world. Crucial that the people of this less accessible area become part of the Chinese development. There would be considerable consequences for the government if there were to be a damaging flood (e.g. in 1981 1.1 million people became homeless). There are 10 million at risk in Hubei Province.

Adverse features/Disadvantages

Social continued
kept. Human rights at risk. Communities and families torn apart.

High rents charged on new (improved) houses.

Economic
Cost of scheme ranges from US25$ billion to US75$ billion! Massive loss of farms with fertile soil, farms and orchards lost. 650 factories to be inundated with loss of many jobs. Massive loss in tourism income. The Three Gorges is one of the world's most spectacular scenic attractions. The cost will put the country into debt for 50 years. By 2004, high sewage levels noted in the river.

Environmental
Water pollution will increase since the dams will now trap pollutants from mines, factories and human sewage. Damage to existing habitats of fish, animals and waterfowl. 1,300 archaeological sites to be flooded or moved. Earthquake zone fear. 530 million tons of silt per year will clog up dam. Flooding will not be eliminated

Political
Major arguments between Chinese government, local groups, environment groups, tourism and human rights groups. No agreement. Opposition suppressed and little freedom to complain.

ENVIRONMENTAL INTERACTION: URBAN CHANGE AND ITS MANAGEMENT

This is a relevant and interesting Environmental Interaction. The main idea is that large urban concentrations, which change in response to a wide range of environmental, social, economic, technological and political factors.

What You Should Know

You need to have detailed case study knowledge about two urban concentrations, one from an economically more developed country (EMDC) and one from an economically less developed country (ELDC). With the EMDC example there is very considerable overlap between this Interaction and the Human Environment Unit Urban and some of that content is relevant to this theme. My case studies will be Glasgow (again!) and Cairo (Egypt).

Remember

I have reviewed every question since 1993. You will be asked questions about urban change both in the EMDCs and ELDCs. The case studies are really important. However the first part of the question tends to be one for 5 or so marks, asking you to write about urban and city growth in a global setting. This unit will look at those global trends, then concentrate on ELDC urban issues. Finally I shall tidy up some EMDC urban changes. Remember that there is overlap with the Environment core unit.

Trends in Urban Population Urbanisation and counter-urbanisation

There have been three main phases in the growth of urban areas (urbanisation). Some 5 or 6 thousand years ago, in areas such as Mesopotamia (mainly modern Iraq) and Egypt, India and China, agriculture surpluses allowed merchants, traders, craftsmen and 'government' officials to concentrate in 'central' areas. During the 18th and 19th centuries, we had the industrialisation of several European countries based on raw materials, trade and economic expansion. More recently we have had the greatest movement of people on the planet, from the rural areas in the ELDCs to the urban areas. In 1801 there was 1 city with a population of over 1 million (London); by 2001 there were 293! By 2001 there were also 33 cities with over 5 million people and 11 with over 10 million.

Population in urban areas (%)	1950	2000	2025
World	30	51	67
ELDCs	17	44	65
EMDCs	53	74	73

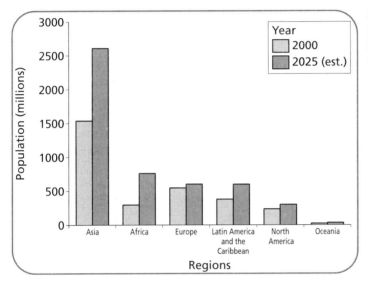

Figure 13.1 Urban population by region, 2000 and 2025 (projected)

Questions and Answers

SAQ 1 a) Describe the changing trend in world urbanisation shown on the table and Figure 13.1

b) Referring to countries or urban areas you have studied, explain this trend in the ELDCs.

c) What is counter-urbanisation? Explain this growing trend in the EMDCs. *(10 marks)*

Answer to SAQ 1

a) Since 1950 to 2000, there was a growth in urbanisation in all regions regardless of level of development. Overall as a world trend the growth has been about 40%, with more than a doubling of the percentage of people in the ELDCs living in an urban context.

The projection to 2025 shows a continuing expansion in the world and a contraction in the percentage from the EMDCs. The expansion continues in the ELDCs with a projected increase of about 50%. The table only gives percentages. It does not give numbers. Since there has been a massive growth in population total, then we need to look at the diagram. This shows that urban growth continues in all regions. The most

Questions and *Answers* continued ➤

Questions and Answers continued

Answer to SAQ 1 continued

rapid rate is taking place in Africa, followed by Asia and Latin America. The rate of growth is lower in Europe and North America. The diagram shows that over 1,000 million people will be added to the urban population in Asia, with almost 450 million added in Africa. In Europe and North America the number added in total will be around 100 million.

b) This answer is really about the reasons for the growth of urbanisation in the ELDCs. The outline below is presented in some detail. You would not be expected to have all this information in your answer. I have given some general outline points. My case study, Cairo, will be featured later on in this section. There are two main processes at work in the ELDCs. Firstly population growth and, secondly, urbanisation pressures should be presented in terms of 'push' and 'pull' factors. You probably first came across this concept in years 3 and 4. It is not new. I have also referred to it within the Population chapter.

'Push' factors

There is great pressure on the land with too many people and overpopulation. There is a division of land leading to too small farms and fields. There is also a higher chance of food shortages, famine, under-nutrition and malnutrition following crop failure, desertification and land degradation. Increasing mechanisation is leading to increased unemployment. Life is hard with low rewards. There is a lack of services (schools, hospitals, electricity, sewage and water supply), poor housing and poverty. There are possible restrictions on religious and political action, with less freedom for gender equality and less hope for children and their future.

'Pull' factors

The perception of a better way of life is a powerful magnet. There are better opportunities for individuals, families and children. There is a chance of factory work with regular wages. There is the perception of better housing, improved services in education and health, with a more reliable supply of food. There is a higher quality of life with adequate water and sewage treatment. People live longer with less oppression and fewer restrictions on freedom. There is also more entertainment and cultural opportunities.

You can apply these factors to any major city you have studied in the ELD world. Apply these key points to specific named examples from your case study. Urban areas are where the key features of 21st century life can be found. This is where technological advances take place and where the economic and political 'power' lies.

c) Counter-urbanisation is the movement out of the city, beyond the boundaries. This process in to be found in the main EMD world. There is a need for (usually the more affluent) people to escape the congestion, noise, pollution, threat of crime and social decay of the city and go to the idyllic rural areas. Some people need more space,

Questions and **Answers** continued ➤

Questions and **Answers** continued

Answer to SAQ 1 continued

(growing families), less need to have access to the CBD (with retirement), and with better transport links, people can still commute into the city to work. There is the attraction of better schooling, lower house prices and lower costs as well as a higher quality of life. The attractions of the city have been diminished while the attractions of the countryside have increased.

SAQ 2 A variation on SAQ 1 parts a and b, could be, 'In 1960, seven of the world's largest cities in the world were in EMDCs. By 2000, eight of the world's largest cities were in ELDCs.' Referring to any cities you have studied, explain the different growth rates. *(6 marks)*

Answer to SAQ 2

The main part of the answer should focus on 'push' and 'pull' factors. However what has happened to EMD cities? Overall there has been slow population growth in such countries as the UK and France. The only other way in which cities can grow is through rural to urban migration. This has also been limited in such countries. Cities are increasingly being viewed as congested, polluted and expensive. Authorities are attempting to prevent urban sprawl and a counter-urbanisation movement can be noted.

Distribution and growth of cities

Questions and **Answers**

SAQ 3 Study Figure 13.2, which shows the distribution of major cities in the USA.

a) With reference to the USA or any other named country you have studied in the ELD or EMD world, describe and explain the distribution of major cites. *(5 marks)*

b) With reference to any named city you have studied in the ELD or EMD world, describe and explain the physical and human factors involved in its growth. *(5 marks)*

Questions and *Answers* continued ➤

Questions and **Answers** continued

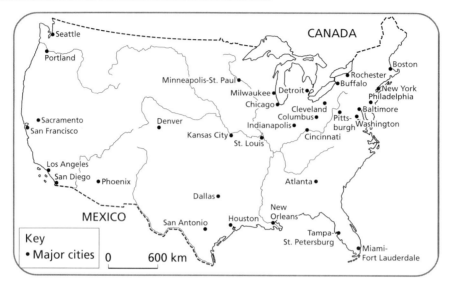

Figure 13.2 The distribution of major cities in the USA

Even though the question may give you visuals about one area, you will have a choice. The key to all of this is that you have case study examples from both ELDCs and EMDCs. I will stick with the UK and Glasgow, and Cairo (Egypt). However since you have been given a map of the USA, let's have a look at an answer.

Answer to SAQ 3

a) The key headings can apply to any country. Note the high number of cities on the coast (e.g. Boston, New York, Los Angeles, Washington) or on rivers, (e.g. Kansas City, New Orleans) or on both. Cities may have a lakeside location (Chicago, Detroit). Cities tend to avoid mountains, deserts, dense forested areas, and be in areas of positive climate, fertile land and near to raw materials and resources. Historical links, bridging points and route centres can also result in development. You should plan out your answer for your chosen country along the lines of my answer above.

b) For a city in a developed country, I have already covered this possibility in the Environment Urban core for Glasgow. Check back now. See the grid ('heads and tails'). Cairo, the 'primate' city and capital of Egypt has a population of somewhere in the region of 15 to 20 million people. Memphis was the ancient capital of the Egyptian empire, and was located among the pyramids on the west bank of the Nile. The east bank developed as a fortress and then a fortified royal enclosure. The city sits across the River Nile, in very fertile farmland (an important factor), is a significant route centre and bridging point. The main growth over the last 50 years has been as a result of rural push and urban pull factors. (These can be developed in some detail.)

The structure of cities in ELDCs, housing quality and 'shanty' town development

We have had a look at urban models in EMDCs. Can we now recognise patterns from the less developed world? See diagram 13.3.

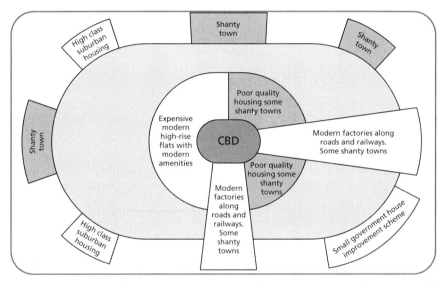

Figure 13.3 Model of land use and residential areas in a city in the ELD world

Questions and Answers

SAQ 4   a)   Describe and explain the main features of this model. Explain the variations in housing quality. *(4 marks)*

b)   With reference to a named city you have studied in a ELDC:

♦   Describe and explain the location and then the growth of shantytowns.

♦   Describe the social, human, economic and environmental problems that have been created by the growth of the city.

♦   Describe the methods used to try to improve the quality of the poorer residential areas.

♦   Comment on the effectiveness of the methods used.   *(16 marks)*

This is a major question, parts of which appear every year. So select your city and put together a detailed answer. I'll cover the general headings, then study Cairo in detail.

Answer to SAQ 4

a)   The model is a combination of concentric rings, showing that the city has grown outwards in sequential stages based on age of development, as well as wedges or sectors, usually along a main road. The structure is different from the EMD world, in

Questions and Answers continued ➤

ENVIRONMENTAL INTERACTION: URBAN CHANGE AND ITS MANAGEMENT

Answer to SAQ 4 continued

that growth here has only been very rapid over the last 30 years. The CBD does exist. The international banks, offices and main shops still have to have a central location. Land values are very high. One notable difference from the EMDCs is that outside the CBD there exists a zone of expensive houses for the wealthy landowners, merchants, administrators and business people. Some modern high rise, quality buildings may have been built recently. Shanty settlements have grown wherever there is space (see below), often very close to the centre, on land unwanted or undesirable or sometimes at great distance from the CBD around the edges of the city. A mixed 'middle 'zone exists where there is a mixture of lower-quality housing and industry. The factories tend to locate along the road and rail lines. In many cities in ELDCs, the quality of the housing can deteriorate as distance from the centre of the city increases. This is where many of the migrants live. In separate communities, you can also find more affluent groups of people. These people may have chosen to live in such locations, free from the worst pollution and congestion. Wealth or even lack of it determines where you live in such a city.

b) **Location of Shanty Settlements**

The model diagram shows a variety of locations. The key to location is land being cheap/available/undesirable. People use incredible imagination and resourcefulness to adapt and organise themselves. The location factors include:

◆ Close to employment opportunities (CBD, Industry/Ports/Railways).

◆ On low cost land

◆ Undesirable sites (refuse dumps/railway sidings/under motorway flyovers/ cemeteries).

◆ Gap sites are steep slopes/disease ridden swamps/end of airport runways/polluted sites).

The growth of shanty settlements

Shantytowns grow as a result of 'push' and 'pull' factors. You can use the information provided in SAQ 1b as relevant to your answer. They are a reaction to high population growth. They attract many migrants with no existing family links to the city. For many people they are no more than a 'stepping stone' to a better way of life. Since the countries will themselves be poor, the shanties are no more than an inevitable reaction to the inability of local authorities to cope with the growth from large numbers of in migrants.

Economic, social, human and environmental living conditions

Sites directly result in overcrowding of an unimaginable degree (e.g. over 10000 people per sq. km. in parts of Mexico City), rapid development without structure or planning, authorities cannot cope with numbers of people. Population is very youthful (over 60% under 15 years in Nairobi). Faced with poor formal employment opportunities (mainly

Questions and **Answers** continued ➤

Questions and Answers continued

Answer to SAQ 4 continued

menial jobs, but a large informal/grey economy exists, (e.g. Karachi). Infrastructure weak. Lack of mains, clean water and sewage; unreliable electricity supply (e.g. Lagos). Transport systems inadequate and cannot cope with the demand. They are often too far away or simply unavailable (Jakarta). Living conditions can be dreadful, with lack of space and privacy and unhygienic, often leading to high levels of disease. High infant mortality and lower life expectancy due to diseases such as typhoid and poor diet (malnutrition). There are insufficient schools (and if they do exist they will be poorly equipped e.g. Lima) and inadequate health clinics, hospitals and medical staff. (Calcutta). The air can be polluted, with noise and water pollution adding to the stresses (Bombay and Rio). The streets are narrow, often unpaved yet crowded and congested (Manila). Such townships can also become centres for crime, disorder and vice (e.g. Soweto).

However such settlements do provide homes and they do supply a need. They can be constructed cheaply and quickly. With their network of workshops and small industries they can provide work, and the closeness of the people allows a community spirit to exist. For many they are temporary and people do move on. While not in any sense ideal, they are at least better than sleeping rough 'on the streets'.

Solutions and methods used to try to improve the quality of the poorer residential areas

Shantytown people can organise themselves into 'self help'/self-improvement groups (especially noted in India and Brazil). This empowerment of the locals, when combined with support from the local authorities, churches or charities (e.g. 'medicines sans frontiere' or Christian Aid) can lead to improvements. There is a lot of work done to tackle the needs of the young. There is a need to get local officials more involved with local projects. To make life better, take each problem and go for the obvious solution. Put in a water supply and lay down sewers, get electricity in to the settlement and construct paved roads with pavements. Health clinics and schools can be built. Indeed there are many examples of such projects going on in virtually every shanty settlement at the moment. A workable plan involves the authorities providing the money but organised local people will supply the labour. However other strategies make sense. It is sensible to reduce the need to migrate by trying to tackle the 'push' factors, and make the rural areas more attractive.

The effectiveness of the solutions

The authorities in many countries also have responded by building 'new towns' and satellite towns to attract the incomers. The trouble is that the more the city authorities do to improve the quality of life in the shanty settlements, then the more attractive they become to potential rural migrants, and the more they will want to come. The more money put into the shanties, then the more they need. There is reluctance from local people to more away from the city centre shanties. Location is important. The pressures remain.

Example: Cairo

Growth. As the city expanded, both squatter settlements and planned projects sprawled across the valuable arable land. Both banks of the River Nile are densely populated, as are the two river islands. The city has extreme contrasts of wealth and poverty. Within a few hundred metres you can move from the shanty settlements to international offices and banks, luxury hotels and restaurants. The quality of life in the shanty settlements can be compared to the general points made above.

Transport. I was in Cairo a few years ago. I was told, 'traffic lights were introduced in 1967 and people have not really got into the habit of looking at them'! The roads are chaotic, congested, polluted and it's almost impossible to find a place to park. The bridges over the Nile, including the newly constructed Al Muneeb Bridge, are choked. In recent years we have seen the development of a Metro rail system. By 2005 there will be over 150 km of track carrying 8 million passengers a day. Fuel is highly subsidised and there seems to be no slowdown in the registration of new cars. There are lots of new roads and flyovers being constructed. River buses help to take people away from the roads.

Water and sewage provision. There is a problem of coping with sewage. Many of the old sewers have collapsed. Following the infrequent rain, there is the chance of floodwater choking the drains and the sewage leaking out. A massive programme has started to deal with this health hazard. The problems affect the poor rather than the rich

Housing. There are 110 squatter settlements around the city, housing 6 million people, many of whom spend their days in search of food, water and jobs.

Half a million people live in the 'City of the Dead'. They live in poor-quality flats and tenements built over graves/tombs. 50,000 people actually live in the tombs and mausoleums in the Arafa cemetery. Such an area although lacking in services does have the advantage of a location close to employment and transport. Cairo has a surplus of housing. There has been considerable construction and speculation. The problem is that the houses are not in the places where people want to live. The new settlements are often remote from the city, from jobs and transport and tend to have been built before the infrastructure (electricity, water and sewers). These flats, visible along all the routes into and surrounding the city, tend to be concrete shells awaiting completion. Flats tend also to be constructed in such a way as to allow extra levels to be added at a later date. Newcomers prefer to join relatives and friends in the already overcrowded squatter settlements and flats.

Pollution. Cairo attacks the senses: noise, smell, visual. 15 million people packed into a restricted area. Vast refuge dumps surround the city. Squatter settlements are found beside these sites, giving many people a source of income recycling the city waste.

Muslim and Christian charity groups are active in organising local action self-help groups to improve local communities. Overall the Cairenes are not interested in collective action.

There are many factories in the city providing jobs for millions of people. However do not undervalue the importance of the informal or 'grey' economy with many people seeking any opportunity to make a living on the streets.

Example continued ➤

Example *continued*

Since the 1970s the government has attempted to halt the growth of the city by building satellite towns, and tried to open up a valley to the west of the Nile in order to attract industry, farming and new settlement. Once again this has had only partial success since people would rather come to Cairo.

Questions *and* **Answers**

SAQ 5 With reference to Cairo:

  a. Describe and explain the location and then the growth of shantytowns.

  b. Describe the social, human, economic and environmental problems that have been created by the growth of the city.

  c. Describe the methods used to try to improve the quality of the poorer residential areas.

  d. Comment on the effectiveness of the methods used.   *(16 marks)*

Answer to SAQ 5

Check my notes above.

Why don't you also take the opportunity to add to my notes by checking information from the Internet?

Urban change in EMDCs

Let's review what we have already covered in the Urban Environment Core Unit. We looked at the site and situation and growth of cities. Our case study was Glasgow. We also introduced the idea that within such cities, distinct urban zones can be identified. The main zones recognised are the CBD, 19th-century housing and industry (a zone often referred to as the 'inner city'), 20th-century housing and industry. Around the city we have open space (greenbelt) Again we looked at Glasgow. Two main areas of change were studied, within the CBD (traffic and shopping patterns) and the Inner City. You can be asked questions about the CBD, housing and the Inner city in this part of the exam. So check back on these notes now!

Land use conflicts and change at the edge of the city

Cities are dynamic. They grow, change and develop with time. Changes take place within the city as well as at the edges or periphery. There is demand for land and conflicts can occur. As we have found out throughout this course, in the face of such change, we attempt to manage and control. It is not possible to keep every user happy, and compromise has to happen. Urban sprawl is taking place in virtually all cities as they expand. It happens in both the less developed world and the more economically developed world. Let's concentrate on sprawl in UK cities.

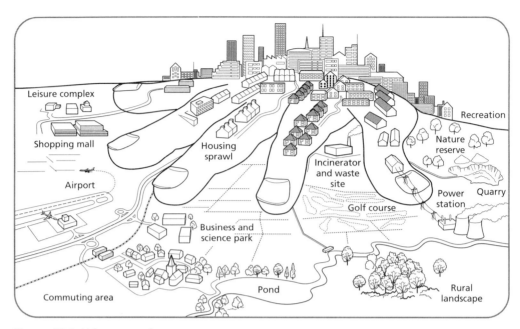

Figure 13.4 Urban sprawl

Questions and Answers

SAQ 6 With reference to Figure 13.4 and to a named city in the EMD world:

a. What land uses are found at the fringe of the city?

b. What are the causes of urban sprawl?

c. What problems and conflicts are likely to occur?

d. What strategies can we use to tackle the conflict and sprawl issues?

e. How effective has this been? *(15 marks)*

The marker has discretion with this question. If no clear named city is identified, then the maximum mark will be 12. All five parts must be mentioned for full marks, with a maximum of 2 marks awarded for the first part, and a maximum of 5 marks for each other part.

Questions and *Answers* continued ➤

Questions and Answers continued

Answer to SAQ 6

Causes

Pressure for outward residential expansion

Growth of villages in the commuter belt

Pressures to improve transport (e.g. ring roads)

Recreational demands for land

Pressure for retail and commercial expansion

Rehousing development from the 'Inner City'

Changes in the CBD

Pressure to find more space for urban waste

Need for other developments (e.g. airport expansion)

Strategies

Planning controls/restrictions/zoning (e.g. creating 'greenbelts'), the creation of a 'master plan'

Encouraging development in other areas through the use of grants and loans, (e.g. Enterprise zones) and encouraging growth at New Towns and through 'overspill agreements'

Encouraging redevelopment of 'brownfield sites' (e.g. Braehead, Glasgow).

Encouraging improvement within the CBD and the 'Inner City' (e.g. the redevelopment of the Gorbals).

Counter-urbanisation strategies to encourage developments within existing boundaries (see notes). If you make the cities more attractive at the core, then there is less need to move people and services to the fringes

Problems

Loss of farmland (often fertile), loss of existing woodlands, school playing fields

Conflicting demand from infill sites and refuge dumps

Conflicting demands for other uses such as recreation, transport, retail, industry, airports. Usually any such development is unwanted by existing users of the land

Loss of community feeling in existing villages

Loss of 'quality of life'

As the city grows at the edges, then the city centre 'dies a little'

Blight of rural/urban fringe with increase in vandalism

Pollution increased (e.g. transport, industry and quarrying)

Effectiveness

The main problem is that there is a demand for new developments (especially housing) and this is difficult to stop.

People generally want to improve their 'quality of life', and the strategies mentioned can really only work with the support of local and national government and with the support from the people

The creation of restrictive zoning has had an impact

There has been too much emphasis on plans, rather than ensuring that they are put into place. Often the plans are too ambitious, and it is not possible to control everything

Often the plan ignores the social and human needs of the people. Experience shows that the plans are too rigid, underresourced and based on incomplete analyses of needs

ENVIRONMENTAL INTERACTION: DEVELOPMENT AND HEALTH

For most students this is a very interesting and enjoyable interaction. The main idea is that there are social and economic development inequalities in the world today. Levels of health and the incidence of disease are major indicators of levels of development. The case studies will be drawn from economically less developed countries (ELDCs).

What You Should Know

You are expected to have a knowledge and understanding of:

◆ A range of social, economic and composite methods of measuring patterns of development,

◆ Differences in levels of development between and within countries,

◆ The physical and human factors involved in the levels of health and the incidence of disease,

Through the study of **one** water-related disease selected from

Bilharzia/schistosomiasis or cholera or malaria

◆ Strategies for improving health and the control of disease.

For most of us living in the UK, 'quality of life' is better today than it was for our great-grandparents. This gives us a basic definition of 'development'. Development can be measured in economic, social and political terms, can change over time and allows us to compare different countries. A fully developed country allows people to achieve their full potential, as well as enjoying health, wealth and freedom.

Development

Indicators of development

Such indicators have several uses

◆ They allow us to compare different countries using standard agreed measurements.

◆ They allow us to rank countries.

◆ They allow us to chart progress over a period of time.

◆ They give us a 'snapshot' of a country, economically, politically and socially.

Some advice. You will be expected to use development indicators, and it is important that you do not become 'sloppy'. Give the full titles and units of measurement. In order to compare countries you need to use percentages, rates per 1,000 and amounts/person. For example, you cannot compare two countries by simply stating the number of doctors, you have to give the number of doctors per 1,000 people. Countries vary in population size.

Development indicators fall into two groups:

1   Economic, which measure wealth and industrialisation of a country.

2   Social and human, which give an indication of quality of life (health/diet/ education).

Questions and Answers

SAQ 1   Suggest one economic and one social/human indicator of development and show how each might illustrate a country's level of development.
(4 marks)

Answers to SAQ1

Gross Domestic Product (GDP) and Gross National Product (GNP). These economic indicators measure the total value of goods and services produced by the country (GDP includes only the goods produced within the country and GNP is goods and services producing income from abroad). Such economic indicators are usually measured in US$ per person or capita. GDP is probably the most used and well-known indicator. A high figure tends to suggest lots of industry/services/wealth. It is fairly easy to calculate using official government statistics. GDP/GNP, however do not show the distribution of wealth. Is there a fair distribution of wealth? It is a very simple figure, e.g. the GDP of Spain in 2002 was $15,000 per person. This does not mean that every one in that country has that 'wealth'. The GDP is an acceptable indicator in countries which have a money economy but less useful in Niger or Chad, where much of the economy is based on subsistence or informal structures. It is now considered more appropriate to go beyond simple economic indicators of wealth and include social and human indicators.

Examples of social/human indicators
Infant mortality
Usually defined as the percentage of children who die within the first year of birth. It is a significant human indicator which correlates with the overall level of health care within a society, as well as suggesting the financial capability of a country to look after its people.

Birth and death rates
The birth rate is the number of babies born per 1000 of the population. A high rate indicates a low level of development, a lack of contraception or the need to have large families. It seems to be linked to poverty. In the ELDCs figures may not always be accurate. A high death rate indicates low levels of health care provision, poor water quality, sanitation and living conditions.

Literacy rates (per cent of the people who can read and write).
A high rate indicates that the country can afford to provide education for its children. However for some countries other skills may be more important, e.g. linked to farming, child rearing.

Questions and *Answers continued* ➤

Questions and **Answers** continued

?

Answers to SAQ1 continued

Composite Indicators

It is generally accepted that individual indicators are of limited value. Individual social indicators are 'average' figures and conceal large variations within/ between countries. A country with an above average calorific intake indicator may have well-fed people, but this does not tell us much about their overall health, education or wealth or social freedom. For that reason it is possible to group together indicators. We shall have a look at two and mention a third.

Human Development Index (HDI)

This composite grouping of three indicators has been used by the United Nations since 1990. See Figure 14.1.

Wealth   income per capita (also linked to purchasing power)

Health   life expectancy at birth

Educational attainment   literacy and number of years of schooling

The scores range from 1 (best) to 0 (poor)

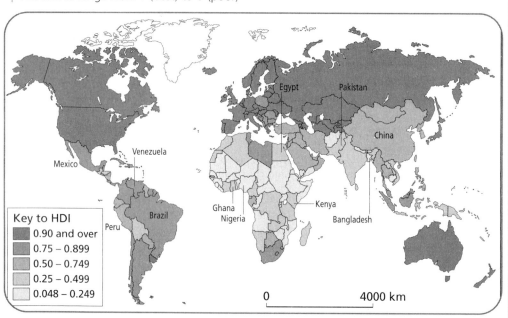

Figure 14.1 Human Development Index (HDI)

Questions and **Answers** continued ➤

Questions *and* **Answers** *continued*

Answers to SAQ1 continued

Physical Quality of Life Index (PQLI) (see Figure 14.2)

Three social/human indicators are rated out of 100 and averaged out. A figure of 75 and below is considered to be unsatisfactory. PQLI seems to be a measure not of the wealth of a country but more the quality of life and this has been improving. For example, Sri Lanka is a poor country but performs well in this indicator with a value of 82. In 1960 53% of the world's population lived in countries with a PQLI of less than 50. In 1990, only 11% lived in countries with such a low PQLI figure. The indicators are:

Life expectancy

Literacy rates

Infant mortality rate

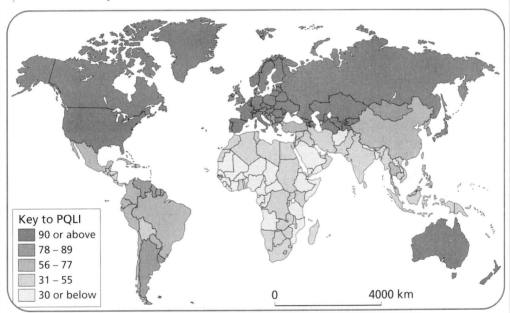

Key to PQLI
- 90 or above
- 78 – 89
- 56 – 77
- 31 – 55
- 30 or below

0   4000 km

Figure 14.2 Physical quality of life index (PQLI)

It is generally accepted that PQLI gives a realistic, yet positive measure of change and success.

A third composite index is the Human Suffering Index. Composite figures rely on a number of valid indicators. They tend to balance out some wide variations.

SAQ 2   Check out the Human Suffering Index on the Internet. Note the 10 indicators used, recognise the top-ranking and low-ranking countries. Would you agree that some of these indicators are very subjective? e.g. political freedom?

Questions *and* **Answers** *continued* ➤

Questions and **Answers** *continued*

SAQ 3   Study Figures 14.1 and 14.2

Identify 10 countries from the PQLI map with a very low index value (below 55).

Describe the pattern of those PQLI areas with the HDI map.

Answers to SAQ3

There is a link between economic indicators (e.g. GDP) and the composite indicators (PQLI). Countries such as Canada, Norway, the USA and the UK will be highly placed in all lists. Such countries use their wealth to provide high levels of education and health care. The opposite is also generally true. That is countries with a low GDP do not have the money to invest in health/ education/infrastructure and have low PQLIs. Some countries do not follow these patterns, e.g. oil-rich Arab states (e.g. Kuwait, Saudi Arabia) with high GDPs (exporting oil) but lower PQLIs.

Or Sri Lanka, China or Costa Rica, with lower GDP but have higher PQLI (such money that there is, is spent on education and health).

SAQ 4   Using either the HDI or PQLI or any other similar combined or composite measures of development:

a.   describe the indicators used to compile the composite measurement, and comment on the usefulness.

b.   outline the advantages of such combined measures.   *(6/2 marks)*

Answer to SAQ 4

Check your answer against the note above.

Contrasts in Development

Why should there be differences in levels of development between countries?

Questions and **Answers**

SAQ 5   Suggest reasons why variations in levels of development occur among the ELDCs.   *(4 marks)*

The notes below feature the negatives which generally 'hold back' development. If you consider the opposite (e.g. a temperate mild climate) then you will have those factors, that encourage development.

Questions and **Answers** *continued* ➤

Questions and Answers continued

Physical factors (can be positive and negative)

Climatic: any extreme will hinder development: for example being too hot, too cold, too wet or too dry. Such extremes will make life difficult. Difficult to build houses and roads, difficult to farm the land, difficult to attract industry and generally difficult to earn a living.

Relief: mountains and steep slopes again make it difficult to farm, live and earn a living.

Natural disasters: those areas likely to be hit by floods, hurricanes, volcanic eruptions, earthquakes or by drought tend to remain less developed.

Other factors: those areas lacking in mineral resources (e.g. coal, diamonds) or areas with poor soils or poor drainage and marshland and those areas that are naturally linked to endemic disease will remain less developed.

Human factors (can be positive and negative)

A high population growth will generally limit development, since increasing resources will have to be spread more thinly (e.g. food, space, jobs, water). There will not be enough jobs, houses, schools, heath clinics. There may well be a low level of industrialisation with few factories and offices. Some people believe that it is commerce and industry that generate the wealth for development, such jobs tend to be well paid and provide security. The ELDCs tend to have jobs in the primary sector, with low levels of trade and often under the influence of the power of the multinational companies. The resulting profits often go abroad and tend not to be reinvested in the country. The ELDCs seem to be burdened with debt repayment and suffer from barriers to trade (tariffs and quotas).

Answer to SAQ 5

The reasons can be taken from the summary notes above.

For example, countries such as Brunei or Kuwait have been able to prosper and develop because of their oil and gas reserves. Countries such as Taiwan, Malaysia and Singapore have developed their industries and prospered (see notes below).

SAQ 6 With reference to named countries, explain why indicators of development may fail to provide an accurate representation of the true quality of life within a country. *(5 marks)*

Answer to SAQ 6

This answer was provided by one of my students.

Socio-economic indicators are average figures for a whole country, and do not reveal internal variations. In India for example, there are great differences between people due to

Questions and Answers continued ➤

Questions and Answers continued

Answer to SAQ 6

rank or status; ethnic origins (are a factor in South Africa). Religious group, political affiliation or inheritance are other possible factors. In oil rich countries such as Kuwait or Saudi, the differences in wealth are massive. The oil is controlled by the ruling class (the oil sheiks). Although the money is spent on health and education, the GDP average is unrealistically high for 95% of the population. Within Brazil there are 'rich' and 'poor' areas, based on differences in terms of climate, relief, vegetation, soils and natural resources. The SE has the resources, the NE is a poor drought-hit area. Average indicators do not allow for regional variations inside a big country. In many ELDCs there is a big difference in wealth and quality of life between the urban areas and the rural villages and farms. India and China are 70 % rural, with the wealth, jobs, best education and higher quality of life concentrated in the urban areas. Once again average indicators do not take this into consideration.

Case Study: Contrasts between ELDCS – Ethiopia and South Korea

This is a study of two ELDCs. Ethiopia a desperately poor country and South Korea an example of a newly industrialised country (NIC), a 'tiger economy' and part of the Pacific Rim. The key points below are generally typical of all similar countries. The table below shows some differences between the two countries.

Questions and Answers

SAQ 7 Study the table in the case study which show indicators of development for Ethiopia and South Korea.

a. Briefly explain why any three of the indicators are useful when describing a country's level of development. *(6 marks)*

b. For either the two countries named in the table or for any other two similar countries, suggest reasons for the differences in development between Newly Industrialising Countries and the ELDCs. *(6 marks)*

Example

Indicators	Sample ELDC Ethiopia	Sample Newly Industrialising Country (NIC) South Korea
People per doctor	13,500	1,100
Life expectancy in years male/female	44/48	70/74
% employed in agriculture	88	50
GDP per capita in US$	410	9,500
Infant mortality (per 1,000 live births)	110	12
Birth rate (per 1000)	44	14
Calories per person per day	2,010	2,500

Ethiopia

Few natural resources. Caught in the vicious circle of poverty. Lack of industrial development. Based on subsistence agriculture with land degradation. Government lacking money and is in debt (10 billion dollars). Suffers from flooding and drought. Civil war and an unstable, corrupt government. Poor health with endemic disease. Level of health poor, as is standards of housing, sanitation and education. Aids/HIV holding back development. High population growth (+3%) with a poor infrastructure. Few powerful 'friends' in the world. Not an attractive area for visitors to visit as tourists.

South Korea

A government, that is politically secure, stable and supportive. Wealth is based on industrial growth. Wealth is reinvested in housing, health, sanitation, and food. Urban-focused with concentrated social service. Foreign investment attracted and multinationals keen to be involved. Naturally occurring resources. Large, flexible, low cost workforce. Labour force also well educated and resourceful. Well located to export to the growth Pacific Rim countries (USA, Japan, China). However note that there is exploitation of some groups (women, children), low wages, health and safety concerns, environmental issues. Able to feed itself. Has powerful allies (USA). Population growth under control.

However, these notes do tend to conceal variations. The indicators are average figures, and there are wealthy groups within both societies as well as poorer groups. The urban areas tend to be better off than the rural areas. Remote areas do not have the same access as the 'core' to water supplies, sanitation, education, health, international aid and power.

ENVIRONMENTAL INTERACTION: DEVELOPMENT AND HEALTH

Example

Case Study Brazil   An example of development contrasts within a country

We have looked at economic, social and human indicators as well as the reasons why these indicators do not always show the true level of development within a country. We have also noted why you get variations in development levels in countries across the less economically developing world. The same factors outlined above which describe why these variations exist can also be applied to a single country. Let's have a look at Brazil (Figure 14.3).

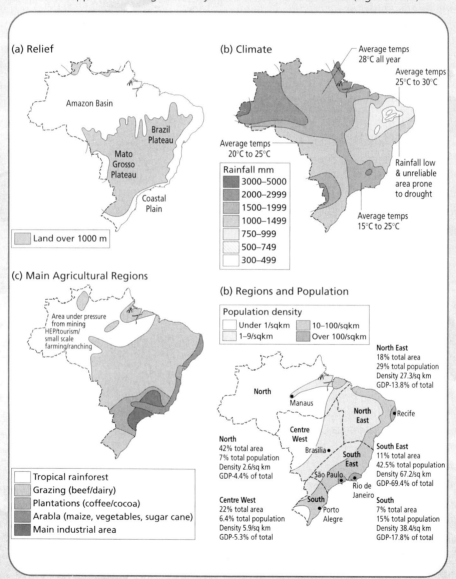

Figure 14.3 Brazil: showing relief, climate, agriculture and population

Example continued ➤

Example *continued*

Regional variations within Brazil

Indicator	South-east	South	Centre-west	North-east	North	Brazil
Households with electricity (%)	98	97	93	77	60	94
GNP per capita (US$)	12,000	9,000	6,500	3,800	4,100	8,000
People per doctor	750	950	2,000	9,800	10,500	2,400
Life expectancy in years	73	72	68	55	55	68

Questions *and Answers*

SAQ 8 With reference to the table above:

a) In what ways does the information given in the table suggest that the five regions of Brazil are at different levels of development. *(5 marks)*

b) For Brazil, or any other ELDC which you have studied, suggest reasons for such regional variations. *(5 marks)*

Answer to SAQ 8

a) This is probably considered to be a straightforward question. You can rank the regions. The 'south-east' appears on all indicators to be the 'richest' region in all four categories, followed by the 'south'. Describe what you see. State the basics. These two areas are the most developed, with more wealth per person and higher levels of education, health and 'quality of life'. The 'north-east' and 'north' are the two poorest areas. The evidence is that only 60% of the households in the 'north', have mains electricity, and the average GNP wealth is about a third of that of the richer 'south-east'. There are very significant differences in access to medical care and life expectancy.

b) The basic structure to the answer is contained in the notes above. The south-east and the south tend to have many positive factors that encourage development. However the north and north-east have many negative factors that discourage development. Figure 14.3 illustrates some of those points. However as far as Brazil is concerned, there is a concentration of industry and commerce in the urban areas of Sao Paulo and Rio de Janeiro. The higher population density figures in the south and south-east encouraged a concentration of economic and social services. The south and south-east have the best soils and the most reliable climate. The north and north-east have negative features in all of those areas. The information clearly illustrates regional variations.

Health

Levels of health and the incidence of disease are major indicators of development. You may wonder why geographers study disease and health. After all, if you were unwell from cholera or malaria, you probably would not ask for a geographer to attend to you and your illness! However, many diseases are linked to the environment, whether it be the physical environment, social/human conditions or to general lifestyle. If we can map patterns and differences then it is geography. We are involved world wide as part of teams of experts trying to eradicate diseases such as bilharzia or malaria. Regretfully such diseases, once established in the human body, are linked to misery, underachievement and may trap a person in a spiral of ill-health, out of which it may be impossible to break.

Summary

A summary of some of the basics

The health of an individual is related to hereditary and biological factors, environmental features as well as social and human conditions. Clearly you would expect a teacher in Scotland to have a healthier life than a beggar in the streets of Jakarta. There are links between certain diseases and population distribution, density and wealth. Disease (or morbidity as it is known in medical statistics) obviously affects death rates and life expectancy. A country with low health care provision is unlikely to have a firm base for economic growth and development.

A summary of factors influencing poor health

Human and Social factors
Poverty (unable to afford health care)
Poor living conditions (e.g. shanty towns)
Lack of sanitation and access to clean water
Insufficient health care support, hospitals, drugs
Low public awareness, poor education, and poor hygiene.
Famine/war/crop failure

Physical factors linked to high death rate and mortality
A climate liable to suffer from drought/flooding, leading to crop failure, leading to famine
Presence of endemic disease
Remoteness

Questions and Answers

SAQ 9 Check your understanding of the following key terms: Endemic disease, Epidemic disease, Jet-borne disease, Pandemic, Endogenous, Exogenous, Starvation or under-nutrition, Malnutrition, Diet deficiency.

Questions and *Answers* continued ➤

HOW TO PASS HIGHER GEOGRAPHY

Questions and Answers continued

Answer to SAQ 9

Endemic disease	A disease habitually present in an area due to permanent local causes, e.g. malaria in tropical West Africa. A person going to Gambia on holiday would know that malaria is to be found here, and would need to take precautions.
Epidemic disease	An outbreak of a disease in an area that is not generally expected to host that disease. For example an epidemic of Asian influenza may hit and spread across Europe to Britain. It is possible for an endemic disease to spread and to become epidemic.
Jet-borne disease	Air travel allows disease to be carried around the world in a short time span. A person coming into contact with, for example, cholera or Lassa fever at breakfast in Lagos could have their evening meal in Glasgow!
Pandemic	An epidemic disease which spreads across a vast geographical area.
Endogenous	A non-infectious illness traditionally associated with the lifestyle of people in the EMDCs (includes cancer, bronchitis and heart disorders).
Exogenous	An infectious or contagious disease such as measles, rabies or cholera.
Starvation/under-nutrition	Simply not having enough to eat.
Malnutrition	This happens when the diet is imbalanced and deficient in one or more of the main food groups essential for a healthy diet, e.g. proteins, carbohydrates, minerals and vitamins.
Diet deficiency diseases	Such as Kwashiorkor, scurvy or marasmus.

Health care must vary accordingly. For example, endogenous disease treatment or prevention can best be tackled by education and by changing lifestyles, as well as by expensive use of drugs, doctors and hospitals. Endogenous diseases can be linked to environmental factors, by poverty and everything that goes with poverty (poor education, health care and unsafe living conditions).

Generally speaking, for the vast majority of countries around the world, people are living longer, death rates are dropping and infant mortality is falling. We seem to be doing something right. However there are massive variations between the EMDCs and the ELDCs.

Nutrition, Health and Development

'There is no drug to solve hunger, still less a vaccine to prevent it' (World Health Organisation).

HOW TO PASS HIGHER GEOGRAPHY

What are the requirements for a healthy lifestyle? Very simply:

◆ A balanced diet to ensure healthy growth and resistance to infection.
◆ Pure water supplies to avoid the dangers from waterborne disease.
◆ Good housing for protection from the extremes of the weather.
◆ An effective health care service for support from pre-birth to old age.

We need to grow more food, improve health facilities, provide clean water and improve health education and provision.

Under-nutrition is essentially not having enough to eat. Carbohydrates, proteins and fats all provide the energy we need. The energy of food is measured in calories and varies according to our sex, age, physique, work and climate. Under-nutrition retards physical development and limits the potential of the human. There is starvation on our planet. However death from total lack of food is becoming rare. When known, the EMDCs tend to get organised and support affected areas through emergency aid action. However under-nutrition, when combined with malnutrition and/or disease, can be deadly. For example in the Gambia, the infant mortality rate from measles is 2.5%. If accompanied by under-nutrition, the rate is 17%.

Kwashiorkor, an example of a disease linked to malnutrition

This disease is linked to protein deficiency. The result is that physical growth is retarded, hair changes colour and may fall out, the stomach is distended and with an overall deterioration in well being. The social importance is that the sufferer is apathetic, unable to work and once a person is trapped, then there is an increased chance of remaining in poverty. It is found in parts of SE Asia, Central and W Africa. It can be prevented by a balanced diet, or partially treated by a synthetic mix of food or eradicated through the elimination of poverty.

Questions and Answers

SAQ 10 Go onto the Internet and gather fact files for two other diseases such as marasmus or scurvy.

A structure of health problems in the ELDCs

It is now a fact that the traditional structure indicated below is changing. Within the ELDCs, there is increasing development with more people having access to a higher quality of life. Patterns of death-related causes are changing. Within Africa, Asia and South America, there is now a similarity with the EMDCs. Heart disease, cancer, cerebrovascular diseases (strokes) and bronchial problems are now very widely found to be a cause of death.

The Higher syllabus asks you to have detailed knowledge about one water-related disease. You should select from bilharzia (also known as schistosomiasis) or cholera or malaria and you should be able to cover all of the following issues.

Questions and Answers

SAQ 11

a) Describe the physical (environmental) and human factors that put people at risk of contracting the disease.

b) Describe the methods and strategies used to control the spread of the disease.

c) Evaluate the success/ failure of these methods.

d) Describe the benefits to the community or county of controlling the disease.
(18 marks)

Normally I would always recommend that you study more than the minimum, i.e. more than one disease. This allows you some insurance in case the question does not suit your study. However in our case study of water-related diseases, you need only study one in depth and have some good case study examples to hand. Let's start by having a detailed look at malaria.

Example

Malaria, 'The King of Diseases'

Location

Now generally to be found within the Tropics, affecting 100 countries and over 2 billion people. In Africa alone, over 400 million people live in areas where malaria is endemic. The location reflects the presence of the parasite-carrying mosquito. This tends to be at altitudes up to 3000 metres.

Temperatures above 16°C and below 30°C, with high humidity, and stagnant pools of water are factors that allow the mosquito to live. These are found in marshes, lakes and river pools. Mosquitoes require stagnant water pools to breed.

Human factors

Marshlands have been drained, dams built, reservoirs created and irrigation ditches dug creating the stagnant water pools. In Vietnam old bomb craters prove rich

breeding grounds for the mosquito. With greater mobility people on the move can transmit the disease to a new area or even reintroduce it into a previously cleared area.

Increasing population growth can encourage people to live closer to affected areas (e.g. close to river pools). Normally the mosquito cannot travel move than 2 km from a water source. Poverty is a crucial factor.

Symptoms

Initially a sore head quickly developing into violent swings between fever and chill, with pain in the stomach. Disease attacks the red blood corpuscles, damages the blood, enlarges the spleen and results in kidney failure. Can be fatal if untreated.

Social impact

Particularly affects the young, who have lower resistance to the disease. Estimated that over one million under fives died in the year 2000. It is socially distressing to see so

Example continued ➤

Example *continued*

many people suffering. When adults are affected the ability to work is greatly reduced. Farm output will be down and there is an increased chance of food shortage. It is reckoned that a country's GNP (from both factories and farms) will be reduced by as much as 25% if the disease is endemic. Following a successful campaign in Sri Lanka, output increased, easily recovering the costs. Money spent caring for the ill could be used for education and general development. Again in Sri Lanka, fertile farmland has been abandoned as people migrate from endemic areas.

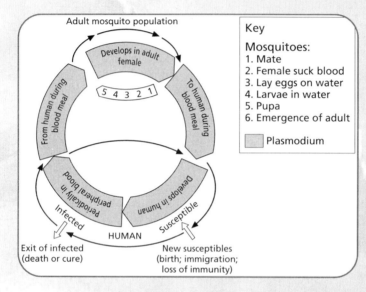

Figure 14.4 Life cycle of the mosquito

Key

Mosquitoes:
1. Mate
2. Female suck blood
3. Lay eggs on water
4. Larvae in water
5. Pupa
6. Emergence of adult

☐ Plasmodium

Although a number of species can transmit the disease, the best-known species is the female anopheles mosquito, which bites an infected person, sucking blood containing the malarial parasite. The mosquito hosts this parasite, and then bites another person, transmitting the parasite into a new victim.

We can attempt to reduce the impact of malaria by avoidance, prevention and control, and by treatment.

Avoidance
Spray planes with insecticide e.g. all planes entering Australia, to prevent disease spreading

Use a mosquito net over a bed, cover windows and doors with gauze and wear protective clothing (the mosquito likes to bite ankles or arms, especially in darkened rooms).

Use insect repellent and spray rooms.

Take drugs prior to travelling to an area (e.g. palodrine or chloroquine).

Keep villages and people at least 1 km away from mosquito breeding grounds.

Prevention and Control
Insecticides such as malathion, dieldron (and formerly DDT) sprayed on ponds, walls, trees.

Drainage of mosquito breeding sites in lakes, pools or irrigation canals.

Example *continued* ➤

Example *continued*

Larvae eating fish introduced to breeding sites.

Spray breeding areas with oil/water based emulsions.

Planting reeds and or eucalyptus trees to soak up excess water.

Flushing streams, by damming then releasing the water, and drowning larvae.

Education programmes run from local villages and PHC schemes.

Reduce levels of poverty. Stronger healthier people can fight off some of the symptoms of malaria better.

Genetic engineering (e.g. create a large pool of sterile male mosquitoes).

Treatment

Anti-malarial drugs that treat the blood parasites within the human (e.g. chloroquine).

Keep up the research for the long awaited vaccine.

Support infected people in health clinics.

What is needed is a commitment from the EMDCs to support the eradication of malaria. This needs money, trained environmental scientists (geographers and biologists), doctors and the organisational skills of groups such as the WHO (World Health Organisation) or the Red Cross. Generally speaking it is best to aim for prevention techniques. However we have hit a number of problems over the years.

An evaluation of malarial programmes

Malaria is endemic over an area affecting more people in 2003 than it was in 1975. The strategy now is for control rather than what the WHO once aimed to achieve, eradication. So what has gone wrong?

It is not all gloom. There have been many successes (within the Middle East, parts of N Africa and parts of South and SE Asia). Over 500 million people have been freed from endemic malaria. The problem is that population growth has been so great in other areas that in total, more people are in danger zones. Fewer people are actually dying from the affects of malaria now than 50 years ago.

Undoubtedly there is an increased awareness by the local people and they generally take all reasonable precautions. Organisations such as the Red Cross are active in providing drugs, equipment and trained people for endemic areas. However the early success in areas such as India in the 1950s have not been maintained. Why? First, programmes are very expensive and cannot always be maintained. When compared with AIDS research, malarial eradication programmes only attract 10% of AIDS funding. Look again at the variety of prevention and control methods. Draining breeding grounds and spraying insecticides is expensive, requires lots of human labour and needs to be organised.

The mosquito has increasingly become resistant to the chemicals used. There is also concern over the wider environmental impact of some of the insecticides used.

The use of anti malarial drugs by people also shows an increasing level of resistance as well as having unpleasant side effects. Genetic engineering may well offer great hope in the future but there is also concern over using new, untested and ethically questionable techniques.

HOW TO PASS HIGHER GEOGRAPHY

Questions and Answers

Answer to SAQ11

This is a very common type of question. Notice that the mark is at the end of the question. This allows the marker to allocate the distribution of the marks more freely. You will need to cover each part of the question, and a minimum number of marks could be awarded to any part. Essentially if you manage to hit 36 relevant points, then you will get full marks! Notice the 'action' words, the words that tell you what to do. Notice that part (c) asks you to 'evaluate'. So what does 'evaluate' ask you to do? It asks you to recognise that there have been both successes and problems linked to the ways in which we have tried to control malaria. You are also expected to give a personal conclusion. This question does not specifically ask you to refer to named case study examples, but if you were to do so then you pick up extra half marks. So always look at ways to name countries and specific programmes.

Check through your own notes on malaria, and my summary notes above. Now answer the question. Allow yourself about 40 minutes. You are expected to write a lot. When you finish check your answer against the notes above, awarding yourself a half mark for every relevant point. That will give you an indication of your overall mark out of 18.

Questions and Answers

SAQ 12 Referring to cholera

a) Describe the physical and human factors which put people at risk of contacting the disease,

b) Describe the methods used to try to control the disease, commenting on their success

c) Explain how the prevention of the disease will benefit people in the ELDCs. *(15 marks)*

Answer to SAQ 12

Study Figure 14.5 below.

Cholera

a) *Physical factors*
Higher temperatures (above 20°C)
Earthquakes/famine/drought affecting water and sanitation
Coastal estuaries (with sources of shellfish)

Human factors
Poor sanitation and waste disposal
Relying on unclean water supply
Sewage mixing with drinking water
Eating sewage-contaminated shellfish
Cooking in contaminated water
Overcrowding and population pressures
Poverty
War and famine affecting water and sanitation

Questions and Answers continued ➤

Answer to SAQ 12 continued

b) *Methods of control might include:*
Care when cooking and washing
Care over personal hygiene after use of toilet
Educational awareness
Vaccinations
Using treated water (boiled, with iodine, chlorine)
Primary Health Care measures (see notes below)
Oral rehydration treatment and saline drips
Control of dumping rubbish and fly control
Public water and sewage treatment schemes
Reduce level of poverty, improve standards of housing, health care

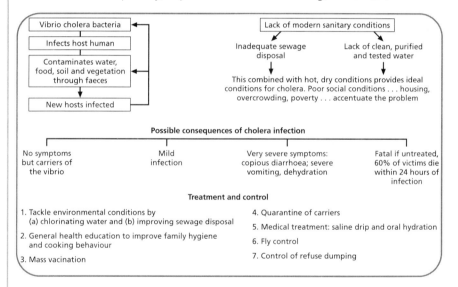

Figure 14.5 Cholera: life cycle

Cholera as an endemic, epidemic or pandemic disease is no longer the threat it once was. Generally speaking, the methods above have been successful. There is awareness of the causes of this disease and following a natural disaster such as an earthquake, the EMDCs tend to quickly support affected areas. Mass vaccination programmes are no longer recommended by the WHO. If medical aid reaches the area quickly enough, it is possible to control cholera. Cholera can be spread by migrants, and until poverty is reduced the disease will always have the potential to flare up again.

c) Cholera not only kills, it also disables people so that they are not able to be economically productive.

Questions and Answers continued

Answer to SAQ 12 continued

If this disease is prevented, money will be able to be used on other health-related problems. The workforce will be more productive, able to increase the overall wealth of the country and increase the GNP, reducing the national debt to the EMDCs. There will be far less individual suffering and previously affected areas may benefit from new tourist related developments.

Global Health Care Models

Figure 14.6 shows a typical health care model for a country in the ELD world.

Questions and Answers

SAQ 13 Describe what you see in Figure 14.6.

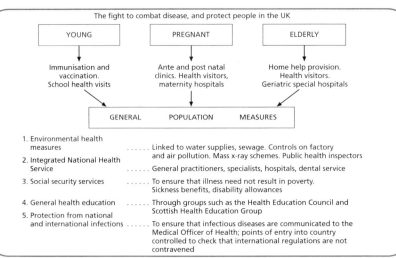

Figure 14.6

Questions and Answers

SAQ 14 Primary Health Care (PHC) strategies have been introduced by many ELDCs in an effort to improve the health of the population.

Give examples of Primary Health Care strategies and comment on their effectiveness in improving health and controlling disease in areas you have studied.   *(6 marks)*

Answer to SAQ 14

PHC aims to make good health care available to all the people in a country. In Nicaragua, the introduction of local health clinics saw a drop in infant mortality (from 30% to 8%).

Questions and Answers continued ➤

ENVIRONMENTAL INTERACTION: DEVELOPMENT AND HEALTH

Questions and Answers continued

Answer to SAQ 14 continued

Mass vaccination eradicated polio and reduced the incidence of whooping cough, and malaria has almost been eliminated. In general, PHC programmes establish health clinics, encourage sanitation and clean water projects. They encourage local village dispensaries using traditional medicines.

The use of 'barefoot doctors', supported by trained helpers can treat over 80% of most illnesses and ill health. Health education projects are linked to local mothers' groups and schools. Local clinics are linked to a referral structure whereby most complex cases can be moved to specialists.

In general, these programmes have been very successful. They involve local people who are known and can be trusted. They are most effective in rural areas that are often remote and isolated, with limited existing educational and medical support.

However too few health workers have been trained to meet the needs of the most troubled communities. There always remains a lack of funding and a lack of volunteers. The early successes have been hit by war, economic depression and natural disasters such as famine or earthquake.

Update: Barefoot Doctor, China

Barefoot doctors were so called because they continued to live and work among local people. Mae Zedong in the mid-1960s recognised that only the urban areas benefited from the existing health care provision, while the rural communities had very limited access to services/ medicine. Large numbers of medical professionals and 'volunteers' were despatched to the countryside to work with the local people. The term 'barefoot doctor' was used to describe those people who assisted with the control of infectious diseases, provided simple effective medical treatment, gave advice on birth control and even assisted with the construction of water and sewage systems. In 1985 the term 'barefoot doctor' was replaced by 'rural doctor' and 'health worker'. By 2003 the system was reported to be in chaos, since the rural health system is now more often than not privately run and expensive for the local people to access. TB is on the increase again, infant mortality is creeping upwards, more women now die in childbirth and immunisation rates are decreasing.

Urban–Rural variation in Health Care ELDCs

| | Access to safe water (1975-2000) | | | | Access to mains sanitation (1975-2000) | | |
| | EMDC e.g. Scotland | ELDC e.g. Nigeria | | | EMDC e.g. Scotland | ELDC e.g. Nigeria | |
		urban	rural			urban	rural
1975	98%	60%	15%		95%	30%	5%
1980	98%	70%	35%		95%	55%	10%
1990	100%	80%	45%		96%	70%	15%
2000	100%	90%	60%		97%	80%	20%

Questions and Answers

SAQ 15 Describe the trends shown in these two tables. *(4 marks)*

Answer to SAQ 15

All levels are higher in the EMDCs. A few remote houses may not be connected to mains sanitation. Urban areas have considerably higher levels. Conditions were very good in 1975, so there is little scope for improvement.

Urban areas in the ELDCs have higher rates than rural areas. All categories show improvement during the data period. More than half of all Nigerians in rural areas have access to safe water, yet main sanitation is still a luxury enjoyed by only 20% of rural people.

When you have data such as this, simply describe what you see, add a few figures for fun and add up the half marks. Easy!

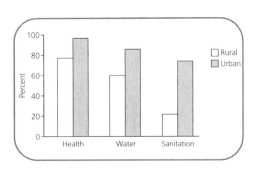

SAQ 16 With reference to countries in the ELDCs with which you are familiar, describe and suggest reasons for the differences in the provision of social services between urban and rural areas. *(5 marks)*

Figure 14.8 Access to social services in the ELDC

Answer to SAQ 16

The problem with this type of question is that there is so much you can write!

Description. You should mention that rural provision is lower than urban provision for all three services. Note that there are variations across the three services, with rural areas being better served for 'health' services, 70% to 90%, while the gap in sanitation service is massive, 18% to 65%.

So what could be the reasons? There are economic reasons for the variations. Urban areas have a concentration of people whilst the rural areas have a more dispersed population. Key workers are far more attracted to urban areas. Political power is often concentrated in urban areas, and that is where most resources will be spent. Rural areas are often remote and isolated, with limited educational support. Once again, a key factor is the level of 'poverty'. Urban areas tend to be less poor, than rural.